這是一本全憑自修就可
完全吸收的最佳參考書

常春藤

英文文法

賴世雄　編著

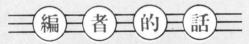
編者的話

　　許多人在學文法時，常覺得記了許多規則卻用不出來，或是在閱讀文法書時，各章節所陳之義雖能瞭解，但在平常閱讀或寫作時，總是遇到許多文法盲點，在屢遭挫折的情況下，很少人能踏踏實實把一本文法書從頭到尾徹底了解。

　　事實上，學語言的人必須先建立一個觀念，那就是，語言本身原本只是現象，並無文法可言，學習語言有如植物生長，本乃自然天成，各位試回憶自己或觀察他人學中文母語的過程中，何嘗有文法可言，而我們在使用母語時卻不會犯什麼錯。因此，我們應秉持一個正確的態度，不要把文法當作標準公式，而應視之為一種啟發概念的工具，平時儘量多讀文章，將閱讀時累積的零碎概念藉著文法知識統整起來，然後再廣泛地閱讀各類文章，將已統整起來的語言架構再印證於實際的英文句構中，如此不斷循環，語言的根苗就在我們的腦子裡生長成形，久而久之，便成軀幹偉碩、枝葉茂密的大樹，此時文法的運用，便是自然而然，無須刻意驅使亦能中規中矩。

　　坦白而言，作者初習英文時，並未鑽研文法，而是先苦讀許多文章，在廣讀熟記的過程中，漸漸發現語言的法則，進而自行加以歸納掌握，最後再看文法書，便覺豁然貫通。然而作者早年在無師指點的情況下，著實曾遭遇許多不易突破的文法盲點，以致也走了不少冤枉路。因此，編著此書時，作者乃儘可能將過去體會過的盲點以清楚易懂的語言澄清，務使諸位讀之即懂，事半功倍。

一般文法書的編排方式，多按八大詞類的順序分項介紹，在這種零散的結構下，讀者即使逐章仔細閱讀，仍難掌握文法的大要。有鑑於此，本書的編排方式採取人類學習語言的自然步驟——先發展軀幹，再衍生枝節。本書內容分上、下兩冊，上冊介紹英文的句型結構，讓讀者先明白如何形成一完整的英文句子，然後進一步點明如何將簡單的句子聯結成複雜而富變化的句子。有了上冊的句構基礎，在下冊的內容中，我們要談文法上其他的重要概念，如時態的運用、比較句構及假設語氣等。至於名詞、介系詞、形容詞、副詞等單元性的內容，也一併於下冊中介紹。據此，本書的上冊可說著重於句構分析能力的建立，而下冊則著重於句構形成後的諸項細則。同學閱讀此書，務必耐心而仔細。為了讓讀者保持輕鬆自然的心情，作者行文之間也不時採用輕鬆詼諧的筆調，然而真正的閱讀樂趣，尚待讀者自行體會。文法本身是枯燥無味的，但如能反覆印證於一般文章中，樂趣便會油然而生。

　　本書原訂今年九月完成，然因作者不斷調整內容架構，多次嘗試以不同筆調編寫，同時參閱許多英、美、日名家的文法書籍，以致一再延誤出版日期，尚請讀者見諒。然而作者相信此書既成，值得讀者欣慰的是，其內容皆為作者多年之學習心得，字字積攢而成。最後，本書之完成，得力於楊平川老師、鄭明俊老師及常春藤編輯部同仁之協助，作者在此謹致謝忱。

目　錄

第六章　時態及語態

第七章　假設語氣

第八章　副詞

第九章　倒裝句構

第十章　比較句構

第十一章　代名詞

第十二章　反問句

第五章
助動詞及易用錯的動詞

第一節　助動詞

概說:

1. 助動詞顧名思義就是一種幫助動詞的詞類。使用時置於動詞前，使動詞能表現出時態、否定句、疑問句等的變化。

  例: I must go at once.
  (我必須立刻走。)

  He used to live in Taiwan.
  (他以前住過台灣。)

  May I go home now?
  (我現在可以回家了嗎？)

  You need not do it.
  (你不必做這件事。)

2. 常用的助動詞有下列幾種:
  be (am, is, are, was, were, have been, has been, had been),
  have (has, had), do (does, did), shall (should), will (would)
  , can (could), may (might), must, ought to, need, dare, used
  為方便同學透徹了解它們的功能及用法，雄哥特別分項敘述如下:

Unit **1**　　Be

1. be 動詞原為不完全不及物動詞(見上冊第36頁)，此時要用名詞或形容詞做補語。

例: <u>He</u>　<u>is</u>　<u>handsome</u>.
　　主詞 不完全 vi. adj. 做主詞補語
　　（他很英俊。）

　　<u>They</u> <u>are</u>　　<u>good students</u>.
　　主詞 不完全 vi. n. 做主詞補語
　　（他們是好學生。）

2. 但 be 動詞之後亦可接現在分詞或過去分詞表進行式或被動語態，此時 be 動詞就稱爲助動詞。

　a. be + 現在分詞 = 進行式

　　例: He <u>is</u>　<u>reading</u> a book.
　　　　　助動詞 現在分詞
　　　　（他正在唸書。）

　b. be + 及物動詞的過去分詞 = 被動語態

　　例: He <u>was</u>　<u>elected</u> chairman.
　　　　　助動詞 過去分詞
　　　　（他當選爲主席。）

　c. be + 不及物動詞的過去分詞 = 完成式

　　例: He　<u>is</u>　<u>gone</u>.
　　　　　助動詞 過去分詞
　　　= He has gone.
　　　（他已走了。）

　　　He　<u>is</u>　<u>graduated</u>.
　　　　助動詞 過去分詞
　　= He has graduated.
　　　（他已經畢業了。）

```
The sun  is  set.
        助動詞 過去分詞
```
= The sun has set.

（太陽下山了。）

＊有關進行式被動語態的用法，我們在時態和語態一章再詳加討論。

Unit 2　Have

have, has, had + 過去分詞形成完成式的時態。

例: He has written the letter.
　　（他已把信寫好了。）

　　I had finished the task before he came.
　　（在他來之前我已完成此工作。）

＊有關完成式的用法，我們在時態一章再詳加討論。

Unit 3　Do

do, does, did 等助動詞可用以形成下列句構。

1. 否定句:

$$\left|\begin{array}{l} do \\ does \\ did \end{array}\right| + not + 原形動詞$$

例: I didn't know what to do.
　　（我不知要怎麼做。）

　　He did not see me.
　　（他没看見我。）

注意:

(1) 任何動詞形成否定時，一定要靠 do, does, did 加上 not

協助，不可造這樣的句子：

例: I not love him.　（×）
→ I don't love him.（○）
　　（我不愛他。）

　　He not lives here.　　（×）
→ He doesn't live here.　（○）
　　（他不住在這兒。）

(2) 動詞前若置除 not 以外的否定副詞如 never, seldom
(不常), rarely (很少), hardly (幾乎不), scarcely
(非常少)等，則不須與 do, does, did 並用。

例: He never lives here. （○）
　　（他從未住過這兒。）
　　He does never live here. （×）

　　He seldom sings. （○）
　　（他很少唱歌。）
　　He does seldom sing. （×）

2. 疑問句：

例: Did you understand it?
　　（你懂嗎？）

　　Where does he live?
　　（他住那兒？）

3. 強勢語氣：
即在肯定句的動詞前，按時態、人稱置入 do, does 或 did
，再將動詞改爲原形。

例: He worked hard.
　　　過去式

(他很用功。)
→ He did work hard.
(他眞的很用功。)

　　He loves to do it.
　　　現在式
(他喜歡做這事。)
→ He does love to do it.
(他的確喜歡做這事。)

注意:
有時命令句 (即一開頭就是原形動詞的句子)，前面亦可加
Do, 造成強勢語氣。

例: Be quiet.
　　(安靜。)
→ Do be quiet.
　　(務必要安靜。)

　　Study hard.
　　(用功。)
→ Do study hard.
　　(務必要用功。)

4 . 否定倒裝句:

例: Never did I know that he was so stupid.
(我從不知道他這麼笨。)

＊容雄哥在倒裝句構一章中，再爲諸位慢慢道來。

5 . 代動詞(pro-verb):
此種助動詞用以代替前句已出現過的動詞及其後的其他詞類。

例: Did you read this book?
　　Yes, I did (= read this book).

(你唸過這本書嗎？　是的，我唸過(這本書)。)

I work as hard as he does (= works).
(我工作和他一樣辛苦。)

Unite 4　Shall, Will

1．shall, will 之後接原形動詞。

2．傳統的文法常在 shall 及 will 做文章，說什麼第一人稱
I 之後須用 shall, we 之後可用 shall 或 will, you 之
後需用 shall...等。現在的英文可沒有如此的用法。而且
英美人士(常春藤語文中心有美國籍、英國籍、愛爾蘭籍、
澳州籍的老師)多已用 will 取代 shall 表單純的未來式。
因此雄哥建議你只須使用 will 就好，既口語又是常態用法
。語文本就是隨著時代而變化，如果一味守著連英美人士都
不用的語法，未免太 "hwen-tan" 了。(hwen-tan 是羅馬
拼音，英文字典裡是找不到的。)

例: I will tell you the truth tomorrow.
(我明天會告訴你事實眞相。)

He will be twenty the day after tomorrow.
(後天他就二十歲了。)

Will you be here tomorrow?
(你明天會在這兒嗎？)
＊上列句構中，不論主詞爲第幾人稱均可用 will。

3．但在下列句構中，則仍習慣用 shall 代替 will:

a. 徵求對方意見時: Shall I...?　　　要不要我……？

例: Shall I open the door?
= Would you like me to open the door?
(要不要我開門呀？)

b. 請求對方合作時：Shall we...?　　　……好嗎？

　例：Shall we go for a walk?
　　　= Let's go for a walk, shall we?
　　　（我們散個步，好嗎？）

c. 命令對方時：You shall...　　　你必須……
　　　　　　　 = You must...

　例：You shall obey the law.
　　　（你必須遵守法律。）

注意：
條約中尤其出現此類用法：

　例：Article One: You（或 One）shall wash your
　　　（或 one's/ his）hands after taking a dung.
　　　（第一條：大便後要洗手。）

d. 向對方保証某種承諾時：You shall...　　　你一定會……

　例：You shall have the present.
　　　= I promise that you will have the present.
　　　（你會得到禮物的。）

Unit　5　　Should

1. should 之後接原形動詞。

2. should 的主要功能就是表示一種義務，譯爲『應當』，此
　 時等於 ought to。

　例：We（You, One, A man）should be kind to others.
　　　（吾人應善待他人。）

3. 但在下列句構時，習慣上亦用 should，有其不同的意思：

a. It is | natural | that...should（會）
        | proper |
        | right |
        | advisable |
        | desirable |
        | no wonder |

……會……乃自然的，適當的，正當的，恰當的，較好的，無疑的

例: It is natural that he should get angry.
（他會生氣是很自然的事。）

It is proper that one who works hard should
be successful.
（努力的人會成功，這是合理的。）

It is no wonder that such a naughty boy
should be punished.
（這樣頑皮的孩子會受到處罰，這是没有什麼好奇怪
的。）

b. It is | necessary | that...should（應當）
        | imperative |
        | essential |
        | important |
        | urgent |

……應當……是有必要的

例: It is necessary that he (should) finish the
work before leaving.
（他必須在走之前完成工作。）

注意:
在本句構中的 should 通常予以省略，而保留其後的原
形動詞。

例：It is important that he finish the job before
leaving.
（重要的是，他必須在走之前完成工作。）

　　It is urgent that he do the work now.
（他現在應該趕緊做這事。）

c. It is | surprising | that...should（居然）
　　　　 | amazing　 |
令人驚異的是……居然……

例：It is surprising that he should be so kind.
（令人驚訝的是，他竟然這麼仁慈。）

d. It is | a pity　　　| that...should（居然）
　　　　 | a regret　 |
　　　　 | regrettable|
令人遺憾的是……居然……

例：It is a pity that he should be so rude.
（他這麼粗魯，真令人遺憾。）

＊見假設語氣一章。

4．意志動詞如表『建議』(propose, recommend, suggest)、
　『要求』(ask, demand, desire, require, insist,
　request)、『命令』(order, command)、『規定』(rule,
　regulate)等，之後若有 that 子句做受詞時，that 子句
　中亦使用 should，而 should 往往亦予以省略。

例：He suggested that we (should) go at once.
（他建議我們立刻去。）

　　They demanded that he (should) be quiet.
（他們要求他安靜。）

＊見假設語氣一章。

5．lest 表『以免』，爲副詞連接詞，所引導的子句亦使用
　　should，而 should 亦可予以省略。

　　例：He came early lest he (should) be late.
　　　 ＝ He came early for fear that he might be late.
　　　（他怕遲到而來得很早。）

＊見假設語氣一章。

6．If 子句若表示與未來狀況相反時，應使用 should，表
　　『萬一』之意。

　　例：If you should be late again, you might spoil the
　　　 plan.
　　　（你萬一再遲到，就會破壞這個計劃。）

＊見假設語氣一章。

7．在過去式的句構中，要使用 should 代替 shall。

　　例：I told him that I should be at home that
　　　 evening.
　　　（我告訴他那天晚上我會在家。）

　　　 I said to him, "I shall be at home this
　　　 evening."
　　　（我告訴他：『今晚我會在家。』）

8．should have ＋ 過去分詞

　　a．表與過去事實相反的假設語氣，譯成『早應……』。

　　　例：If you had not helped me, I should have died.
　　　　（你當時要是沒救我，我就死了。）

You should have done it earlier.
(你應該早點兒做好的。)

It was such a fine sight. You should have seen it.
(這麼好的景色,你當時真該看看的。)

b. 表『居然已經』,往往出現在下列句構中:

例: It is surprising that he should have passed the examination.
(令人驚訝的是他居然已通過了考試。)

It is a pity that he should have done such a stupid thing.
(真遺憾他竟然做了這麼愚蠢的事。)

Unit 6 Would

1. 表過去未來式,與另一過去式動詞並用。

例: He said that he would try again.
(他說他會再試試。)

He said, "I will try again."
(他說:『我會再試試。』)

Did you know when he would come?
(你當時知道他何時會來嗎?)

注意:
新聞英語中,常出現 will 與過去式動詞並用的現象。

例: He said that he will visit the country sometime in June.
(他說七月份要找個時間去鄉下。)

本句暗示 He said 雖為過去狀態，但 he will visit...
則表示未來一定會發生的狀態，在文法上並未有誤。為了方
便你的了解，雄哥特編了下列兩段對話：

會話一： A: I saw John a few days ago.

B: What did he say?

A: He said that he would call on you
yesterday.

B: But as far as I know, he didn't

show up yesterday.

A: 幾天前我看到約翰。

B: 他說了些什麼？

A: 他說昨天要拜訪你。

B: 但是就我所知，他昨天並沒有出現。

會話二： A: I saw John a few days ago.

B: What did he say?

A: He said that he will call on you
tomorrow.

B: I'll be expecting him then.

A: 幾天前我看到約翰。

B: 他說了些什麼？

A: 他說明天要去拜訪你。

B: 到時候我會等他的。

2 . would + 原形動詞　　　　　如果……就會
would have + 過去分詞
表假設語氣，分別表與現在和過去事實相反。

例: a . 與現在事實相反:

If I had money now, I would buy a car.
(But I don't have money now.)
（如果我現在有錢，我要買部車——但我現在沒錢。）

b . 與過去事實相反:

If I had had money then, I would have bought a car.
(But I didn't have money then.)
（當時我要是有錢，早就買車了。）

＊見假設語氣一章。

3 . would rather + 原形動詞　　　寧願

例: I would rather go than stay here.
= I would sooner go than stay here.
= I would as soon go as stay here.
= I would as lief go as stay here.
（我寧願走也不要留在這兒。）

4 . | I would rather | + (that) 子句
  | Would |
  | I wish |
與現在事實相反，that 子句用過去式時態; 若與過去事實相反，則用過去完成式時態。

例: | I would rather | that | he were here. |
| Would | | he had time. |
| I wish | | |

(But he is not here.)
(But he doesn't have time.)
（我真巴不得他　人在這兒／有時間
　——但他　不在這兒／沒有時間。）

I would rather he had been here.
(But he wasn't here.)
（當時我真巴不得他在這兒——可是他當時並不在。）

I would rather he had had time.
(But he didn't have time.)
（當時我真巴不得他有時間——但是當時他沒空。）

5. Would you mind + | Ving | ?　　您介不介意……?
| if 子句 |

= Do you mind + | Ving | ?
| if 子句 |

例: Would you mind | doing it for me?
| if you did it for me?

= Do you mind | doing it for me?
| if you do it for me?

（請您幫我做這事好嗎？）

注意:

a. Would you mind 的口氣要比 Do you mind 客氣。

同理
Would you please do it for me? 要比
Will you please do it for me? 語氣客氣得多。
（請您幫我做這事好嗎？）

b. Would you mind 之後 if 子句中，動詞須使用過去式，

以便與過去式的 Would 配合。Do you mind 之後的 if
子句中，動詞要使用現在式，以便與現在式的 Do 配合。

Unit 7　Can (Could)

1．表『能力』(= be able to)，譯成『能夠』。

例: He can cope with the problem.
　= He is able to cope with the problem.
　(他能夠處理這個問題。)

2．表『可能性』，譯成『有可能』。

例: He can be wrong ┃ to say so.
　　　　　　　　　　┃ if he says so.
　(他要是這麼說就可能錯了。)

3．表『許可』(= may)，譯成『可以』。

例: You can go home now.
　(你現在可以回家了。)

　You can't smoke here.
　(你不可以在這兒抽煙。)

4．在疑問句或否定句中，表『可能性』，譯成『有可能』或
　『不可能』。

例: Can it be true? No, it can't be true.
　(這可能是眞的嗎？ 不，這不可能是眞的。)

5．表對過去事物的否定推論:

can't have + 過去分詞　　不可能曾⋯⋯

例: He is so honest that he can't have stolen your

money yesterday.
(他這麼老實不可能昨天會偷你的錢。)

注意:
a. 表對過去事物的肯定推論, 有兩種句型:

　(1) must have + 過去分詞　　一定曾經……

　　　例: He looks nervous; he must have stolen
　　　　　your money.
　　　　　(他看起來緊張ㄅㄅ的, 一定是偷了你的錢。)

　(2) may have + 過去分詞　　可能曾經……

　　　例: He may have studied hard when young.
　　　　　(他年輕的時候可能很用功。)

b. 疑問句中表對過去事物的推論, 則用 Can...
　　have + 過去分詞?

　　例: Can he have done it?
　　　　(他有可能做過此事嗎?)

6. could 為 can 的過去式, 通常與另一過去式動詞並用, 用
　以表示過去的狀況。

　例: She could speak English well when she was ten.
　　　(她十歲時英文就說得很好了。)

　　　When she entered the house, she could smell
　　　something burning.
　　　(她走進屋子時, 聞到有東西燒焦了。)

7. 一如 would, could 亦可使用在問句中, 以表示客氣的語氣。

例：｜Could｜ you please do it for me?
　　｜Would｜
（請你幫我做這事好嗎？）

8. could = was able to
使用於過去式中，表示過去的能力。

例： When young, he could eat eight bowls of rice at
a time.
（他年輕時可以一次吃八碗飯。）

9. can 與 not 並用時，不要寫成 can not，而要寫成 cannot
或 can't。

例： He ｜cannot｜ write letters.　（○）
　　　｜can't｜
（他不會寫信。）

He can not write letters. （非習慣用法）

注意：
could 與 not 並用時，則應寫成 could not 或
couldn't，不要寫成 couldnot。

10. 有關 can 的慣用語：

a. I ｜can but｜ do so.
　　｜can only｜
（我只能這麼做。）

b. I cannot but laugh.
= I cannot help but laugh.
= I cannot ｜help｜ laughing.
　　　　　｜resist｜
（我忍不住大笑。）

c. We cannot be too careful in choosing our friends.
(我們在擇友時要愈小心愈好。)

d. I couldn't care less.
(我一點兒都不在乎。——我已經不在乎到了極點，因此我不能再少一點的不在乎了。)

e. I couldn't agree more.
(我同意極了。——我已經同意到了極點，因此我不能再更加地同意了。)

Unit 8 May (Might)

1. may, might 之後接原形動詞。

2. 表『許可』，譯成『可以』。

例: You may take whatever you like.
(你喜歡什麼就可以拿什麼。)

May I go home?
(我可以回家嗎？)

Might I make a suggestion?
(我可以提出一個建議嗎？)

注意:
might 與 would, could 一樣，在問句中使用過去式，有客氣的語氣。

3. 表『推測』，譯成『可能』，此時等於 can。

例: It may be ture.
(這或許是對的。)

He may come, or he may not (come).

= Perhaps he will come; perhaps he will not (come).
(他也許是會來，也許不會。)

4．may not 有兩種意思:

  a. 可能不會

    例: It's getting late; he may not come.
    (愈來愈晚了，他可能不會來了。)

  b. 不可以 = must not

    例: You | may not | cheat during the exam.
          | must not |

    (你不可以在考試中做弊。)

5．might 亦可與另一過去式動詞並用，以表示過去的狀況。

  例: He said that I might go.
  (他說我可以走了。)

  He said, "You may go."
  (他說:『你可以走了。』)

  I thought that it might rain.
  (我當時認為可能會下雨。)

6．might + 原形動詞
  might have + 過去分詞
  可用於假設語氣中，分別表示與現在事實及過去事實的相反。

  a. 與現在事實相反:

    if 子句中的動詞使用過去式。

    例: If he tried hard, he might succeed.

(But he doesn't try hard.)
(假如他努力，也許會成功——但他並未努力。)

b. 與過去事實相反：

if 子句中的動詞使用過去完成式。

例: If he had tried hard, he might have succeeded.
(But he didn't try hard.)
(假如當時他努力，早就成功了——但他當時並未努力。)

7. 有關 may 的慣用語：

a. may well　　大可，是有理由

例: He may well be proud of his son.
(他的兒子值得他驕傲。)

b. may as well　　最好……
= had better

例: You may as well stay home.
(你最好留在家中。)

c. may as well...as...　　與其……不如……
= had better...than...

例: You may as well stay home as go out with them.
= You had better stay home than go out with them.
(你與其和他們出去，不如留在家裡。)

注意:
may as well...as... 表較大的可能性，
might as well...as... 則表較小的可能性，
均等於 had better...than...。

例: You might as well die as make friends with
Mary.
(你與其和瑪麗交朋友倒不如死去算了。但我
相信你不太可能去死。)

Unit 9 Must

1. must 之後接原形動詞。

2. 表『義務』，譯成『必須』。

例: You must finish the work before leaving.
(你一定要在離開前完成工作。)

3. must 與 have to 的比較:

a. must 表示一種道德上的必須，而 have to 則有勉強的
意味，譯成『不得不』。

例: You must love your country. (佳)
(你必須愛自己的國家。)

You have to love your country.
(你得愛國——暗示你並不愛國，但非得愛國不可。)

b. must 只能用於表現在或未來的狀況; 而 have to 則可
用於表過去、現在及未來的狀況。

(1) must

例: 現在: You must come now. (○)
(你現在必須來。)

未來: You must come tomorrow. (○)
(你明天必須來。)

過去：You must come yesterday. (×)
(你昨天必須來。)

(2) have to

例：過去：He had to come yesterday.
(他昨天非來不可。)

現在：He has to come now.
(他現在非來不可。)

未來：He will have to come tomorrow.
(他明天非來不可。)

c . 否定時：
(1) must not 不可能
= may not

例：You must not do it.
(你絕不可做這事。)

(2) don't have to 不必
= need not

例：You don't have to do it.
(你不必做這事。)

d . 在口語中，have to 經常被 have got to 或 gotta
取代。

例：I have to tell you the truth.
= I've got to tell you the truth.
= I gotta tell you the truth.
(我得告訴你事實真相。)

4 . must 亦表示對現在狀況或過去狀況的推論。

a. 對現在狀況的推論:

must + 原形動詞　　一定……

例: It must be true.
= It is surely true.
（這一定是真的。）

b. 對過去狀況的推論:

must have + 過去分詞　　一定曾經……

例: It must have rained last night.
= It surely rained last night.
（昨晚一定下過雨。）

Unit 10　Ought

1. ought 須與不定詞 to 並用，之後接原形動詞，
即: ought to + 原形動詞。

2. ought to 可表『義務』，譯成『應當』，等於 should。

例: You │ought to│ be kind to others.
　　　　│should │
（你應該要和善待人。）

You │ought not to│ talk like that.
　　│shouldn't　 │
（你不該那樣說話。）

3. ought to 亦可表『推論』，譯成『應當會』。

例: Since he works hard, he │ought to│ succeed.
　　　　　　　　　　　　　　│should │
（由於他很努力，應該會成功。）

4 . ｜ought to｜ have + 過去分詞
　　｜should　｜
　　形成與過去事實相反的假設語氣。此時 if 子句中的動詞要
　　用過去完成式。

　　例: If he had worked hard, he ｜ought to｜ have been
　　　　　　　　　　　　　　　　　｜should　｜
　　　successful.
　　　（如果他當時努力，應該早就成功了。）

5 . ｜ought to｜ have + 過去分詞
　　｜should　｜
　　亦可表示『推論至目前為止已完成的動作』。

　　例: He ｜ought to｜ have arrived in New York by now.
　　　　　｜should　｜
　　　（他現在應該已到達紐約了。）

Unit 1 1　Need

1 . 在肯定句中, need 為一般動詞，有人稱和時態的變化，譯成
　　『必須』，之後接不定詞片語或名詞做受詞。

　　例: He needs to go.
　　　　　　　　 不定詞
　　　（他必須走。）

　　　He needs my help.
　　　　　　　　 名詞
　　　（他需要我的幫助。）

注意:
某物需要某種方法處理時, need 之後可接不定詞片語，但
一定為被動語態，或接動名詞但一定為主動語態。

例: The car needs to be cleaned.
　　　　　　　　不定詞
= The car needs cleaning.
　　　　　　　動名詞
(這部車需要清洗。)
The car needs being cleaned. (×)

The window needs fixing.
(這窗子需要修理。)
The window needs being fixed. (×)

2. 否定句中, need 為助動詞, 句型如下:

need not + 原形動詞

例: He need not go.
(他不必去。)
He need not to go. (×)
He needs not go. 　(×)

但: He need not go.
= He doesn't need to go.

3. 表過去狀況時:

a. didn't need to 　　當時不必……(而且亦未……)

例: He didn't need to attend the party, so he
stayed home.
(當時他不必參加宴會, 所以就留在家裡。)

b. need not have + 過去分詞　　當時不必……(但卻……)

例: He needn't have attended the party, but he
went there just the same.
(當時他可以不必參加宴會, 但他還是去了。)

4．在疑問句中，need 做一般動詞或助動詞皆可。

　　例: Does he need to go? (一般動詞)
　　　= Need he go?　　　　　 (助動詞)
　　　(他需要去嗎？)

5．注意 need 在反問句中的變化:

　　a．一般動詞
　　　例: He needs to go, doesn't he?
　　　　 (他必須去，不是嗎？)

　　　　 He doesn't need to go, does he?
　　　　 (他不必去，對吧？)

　　b．助動詞

　　　例: He need not go, need he ?
　　　　 (他不必去，對嗎？)

Unit 1 2　Dare

1．dare 可做助動詞，用於否定句或疑問句中。

　　dare not + 原形動詞　　　　不敢

　　Dare one + 原形動詞?　　　敢……嗎？

　　例: He dare not go.
　　　 (他不敢去。)
　　　　He dares not go. (×)

　　　　Dare he go?
　　　 (他敢去嗎？)

2．How dare + 一般敘述句?　　……怎敢……?

例: How dare you say such a thing in my face?
（你怎敢在我面前說這種話？）

3．在 whether 子句中, dare 亦可做助動詞。

例: I wonder whether he dare do it.
（我懷疑他敢不敢做這事。）

4．在肯定句中, dare 為一般動詞, 有時態和人稱的變化, 之
　　後接 to 不定詞。

例: He dares to go. （現在）
（他敢去。）

He dared to go. （過去）
（當時他敢去。）

5．dare not + 原形動詞
　= do not dare (to) + 原形動詞

例: He dare not answer the phone.
　= He doesn't dare (to) answer the phone.
（他不敢接電話。）

I have never dared (to) speak to him.
（我從來不敢與他說話。）

6．dare 亦可做及物動詞, 表『向某人挑戰』之意,
　　句型如下:

dare + 人 + to + 原形動詞

例: He dared me to jump the stream.
（他向我挑戰跳過這條溪。）

7．I daresay + that 子句　　我敢說……

例: I daresay (that) he will be late again.
(我敢說他又會遲到。)

Unit 13　Used

1. used 一定要與不定詞 to 並用，之後接原形動詞，
句型如下:

used to + 原形動詞　　過去曾經……

例: He used to live here.
(他以前住過這兒。)

I used to call on him every Sunday.
(我以前每個星期天都去拜訪他。)

There used to be a big tree here.
(這兒以前有一棵大樹。)

2. 由於 used 可為助動詞，故我們要注意，其在問句及否定句
中的用法。

例: There used to be a pond in this garden.
(這個園子裡以前有個池塘。)
→ Used there to be a pond in this garden?
(這個園子裡以前有池塘嗎?)

I usedn't to like coffee, but I'm quite fond of
it now.
(我以前不喜歡咖啡，但我現在很喜歡了。)

注意:
used to 的主詞若為人時，問句中有兩種變化:
例: He used to work hard.
　　人
(他以前很用功。)

→ Used he to work hard?
或 Did he use to work hard?
（他以前很用功嗎？）

3. 在下列句構中，used 非助動詞，而是 use 的過去分詞：

a. 人 + be <u>used to</u> + | 名詞　| 習慣於……
　　　　　 adj. 介 　 | 動名詞 |

本句構中的 used 是形容詞，譯成『習慣的』，之後
的 to 為介系詞，譯成『針對』。

例: <u>He</u> is used to <u>working</u> alone.
　　人　　　　　　 動詞
（他習慣單獨工作。）

<u>He</u> hasn't | been | used to <u>city life</u> yet.
人　　　　　 | got　|　　　　 n.
（他還不習慣都市生活。）

<u>He</u> is used to speaking aloud.
人
= He is accustomed to speaking aloud.
= He has accustomed himself to speaking aloud.
（他習慣大聲說話。）

b. 物 + be used to + 原形動詞　　被用來……

本句構中的 used 是過去分詞，置於 be 動詞之後，
表被動語態，譯成『被用來』，之後的 to 為不定詞，
其後接原形動詞。

例: The book can <u>be used to</u> <u>teach</u> us English writing.
（這本書可用來教我們英文寫作。）

Much energy <u>was used to</u> <u>deal</u> with the problem.

（許多精力都用來處理此問題。）

c. 物 + be used as + 名詞　　被用做為

例: The knife <u>was used as</u> a weapon.
　　　　　　　　　　　n.

（這把刀被用來當武器。）

不可寫成:
The knife was used <u>to be</u> a weapon. (×)

第二節

易用錯的動詞

1 . lie vi. 躺 (其後不加受詞)
   動詞變化為 lay, lain, lying。
   lay vt. 放置; 生產 (其後加受詞)
   動詞變化為 laid, laid, laying。
   lie vi. 說謊 (其後不加受詞)
   動詞變化為 lied, lied, lying。
   注意:
   lay 為及物動詞, 可用被動語態。

   例: a. He will lie on the desk for a while.
         (他將躺在桌上片刻。)
         He lay on the desk for a while.
         He has lain on the desk for a while.
         He has been lying there all day.

      b. He will lay a book on the desk.
                    ‾‾‾‾
                    受詞
         (他將放一本書在桌上。)
         He laid a book on the desk.
         He has laid a book on the desk.
       = A book has been laid on the desk.
         A book has been lain on the desk. (×)

      c. Don't lie to me.
         (別對我撒謊。)
         He lied to me.
         (他對我撒謊。)

2 . sit vi. 坐 (其後不加受詞)
   動詞變化為 sat, sat, sitting。

set vt. 安置
動詞變化為 set, set, setting。
seat vt. 使坐, 容納
動詞變化為 seated, seated, seating。
注意:
set 和 seat 為及物動詞, 其後須加上受詞, 亦可用被動語態。

例: He came in and sat down.
　= He came in and seated himself.
　= He came in and was seated.
　(他進來, 並坐了下來。)
　　He came in and seated down.
　　(×, seated 之後應加受詞, down 應刪去)

　　He set the table for dinner.
　(他擺桌子準備吃晚飯。)
　　He sat the table for dinner. (×)

　　The movie house can seat two hundred people.
　　(seat = accommodate, 表『容納』。)
　= It can be seated for two hundred.
　(這家戲院可容納二百人。)

3. rise vi. 起床; 升起 (其後不加受詞)
動詞變化為 rose, risen, rising。
raise vt. 舉起; 飼養
· 動詞變化為 raised, raised, raising。
arise vi. 起床; 起源 (其後不加受詞)
動詞變化為 arose, arisen, arising。
arouse vt. 激起
動詞變化為 aroused, aroused, arousing。
注意:
raise 和 arouse 為及物動詞, 其後須接受詞, 亦可用被動語態。
例: He rose at 7 every morning.
　= He arose (較正式) at 7 every morning.

（他每天早上七點起床。）

The sun rises in the east.
（太陽從東方升起。）
The sun raises in the east. (×)
The sun arises in the east. (×)

Accidents | arise from | carelessness.
          | result from |
（意外源於粗心。）

Raise your hand if you have any questions.
（有任何問題請舉手。）

Many cattle are raised on this farm.
（有許多牛飼養在此農場。）

4. hang vt. & vi. 掛
   動詞變化為 hung, hung, hanging。
   hang vt. 吊死
   動詞變化為 hanged, hanged, hanging。

例: The picture hangs on the wall.
  = The picture is hung on the wall.
   （圖片掛在牆上。）

   Tom Dooley was hanged.
   （湯姆杜利被吊死了。）

   They hanged the murderer yesterday.
   （昨天他們把凶手吊死了。）

   The picture is hanged on the wall. (×)
   The robber was hung. (×)

5. fly vi. 飛

動詞變化爲 flew, flown, flying。
flow vi. 流
動詞變化爲 flowed, flowed, flowing。

例: The airplane flew high in the sky.
(飛機在空中高飛。)

This is the place from which the river flows.
(這就是這條河流出的地方——發源地。)

The bird flowed all the way here from Canada.
(×, 應改爲 flew)
(鳥兒從加拿大一路飛到這兒。)

6. take　　　(從近處) 拿去
   bring　　　(從遠處) 拿來

例: Take the book to the library, please.
(請把書拿去圖書館。)

Bring them back here.
(把他們帶回這裡來。)

Take him in my office. (×, Take 應改爲 Bring)
(帶他到我的辦公室來。)

Take it with you when you go there.
(你去那裡時，把這帶著。)

Bring it with you when you come here.
(你來這裡時，把這帶著。)

7. refuse (拒絕) 之用法:

　a. refuse + 名詞

例: He refused my suggestion.
= He rejected my suggestion.
（他拒絕我的建議。）

b. refuse + to + 原形動詞
注意:
refuse 之後不可加動名詞。

例: He refused to go with me.
He refused going with me. (×)
（他拒絕和我走。）

c. refuse 之後不可接 that 子句。

例: He refused that he had done something wrong.
(×)
He denied that he had done something wrong. (○)
= He refused to admit that he had done something
wrong. (○)
（他拒絕承認做錯事。）

8. 人 + spend + 時間 (或金錢) + | 動名詞
| on + 名詞 |

例: I spent two hours writing this letter.
I spent two hours to write this letter. (×)
（我花兩小時寫這封信。）

I spent all my income buying books.
= I spent all my income on books.
（我將所有的收入花在買書上。）

9. It takes + 時間 + to V
It costs + 金錢 + to V

例: It takes (me) about two hours to go from here to

Taichung.
(從這裡到台中花了我兩個小時。)

It cost (me) five dollars to buy that book.
I cost five dollars to buy that book. (×)
(買那本書花了我五塊錢。)

10. answer + 受詞   回答
 = reply + <u>to</u> + 受詞
          介

例: He failed to answer her question.
  = He failed to reply to her question.
   (他未能回答她的問題。)
    He failed to reply her question. (×)

11. reach + 受詞   到達
 = arrive + | in (大地方) |
            | at (小地方) |
 = get to + 受詞

例: I | reached | Chicago at 12.
     | arrived in |
     | got to |
   (我十二點到達芝加哥。)

注意:
與副詞 home, there, here 等連用時，一律不加介詞。

例: I | reached there | at 12.
     | arrived there |
     | arrived at there | (×)
     | got there |
     | got to there | (×)
   (我十二點到達那裡。)

１２. 動詞 + 介副詞 + 受詞 (普通名詞，專有名詞)
　 = 動詞 + 受詞 (普通名詞，專有名詞，代名詞) + 介副詞

例: We have to carry out that mission.
　 = We have to carry that mission out.
　 = We have to carry it out.
　 (我們必須執行那項任務。)

注意:
代名詞一定要置於介副詞之前。
故 We have to carry out it. (×)

類似此類構造的動詞片語如下:

bring up	扶養	hand in	交出
call down	斥責	look over	檢查
call off	取銷	look up...in	查(生字、電話號碼等)
cross out	刪去	make out	了解
do over	再做	pick out	挑選
figure out	想出	pick up	拾起
give up	放棄	put off	延期
put out	熄滅	put on	穿
take off	脫掉(衣服)	try out	試驗(機器等)
take over	接管	turn down	拒絕
talk over	商討	turn in	交出
think over	考慮	turn off	關上
think up	設計	turn on	打開(開關等)
try on	試穿(衣服等)		

１３. 動詞 + 介詞 + 受詞 (普通名詞，專有名詞，代名詞)

例: I called on John yesterday.
　 = I called on him yesterday.
　 (我昨天拜訪他。)
　 I called him on yesterday. (×)

類似此結構的動詞片語如下:

call for	取(東西)	go over	複習
come across	偶然遇見	go through	檢查
= run into		keep on	繼續
= meet...by chance		look after	照顧
get over	復原	look for	找尋
= recover from		look into	調查
get through	做完	take after	像

１４. 重要的『動詞＋介詞＋名詞（代名詞）』之片語:

a. agree on (對條約、定義) 同意

> 例: We do not agree on this term.
> (我們不同意此條件。)

b. agree to (對事) 同意

> 例: I agree to his coming here.
> (我同意他來。)

c. agree with (對人) 同意

> 例: I agree with him on this point.
> (關於這點，我同意他。)

d. consist of 包括

> 例: This class consists of 10 students.
> = This class is composed of 10 students.
> = This class is made up of 10 students.
> (這班共有十個學生。)

e. argue with (與人) 爭論
argue over (就事) 爭論
approve of 贊同

```
        care for      喜歡
        complain about （或 of ）抱怨
        consent to 同意
        comment on 評論
        count on      依賴
    = depend on
    = rely on
        hear from        聽到某人的回音; 接到某人的來信
        laugh at         取笑
```

１５. 重要的『動詞 + 受詞 + 介詞 + 受詞』之片語:

　　例: Add this number to that number.
　　　 （將此數與該數相加。）

　　　 He blamed me for the fault.
　　　 （他把錯歸咎於我。）

　　　 I congratulated him on his success.
　　　 （我恭賀他的成功。）

　　　 He explained it to me.
　　　 （他向我解釋此事。）

　　　 He won't excuse me for being rude.
　　　 （他不原諒我的粗魯行為。）

１６. 重要的三字（三字以上）動詞片語:

　　例: He fell in love with Mary.
　　　 （他愛上了瑪莉。）

　　　 He will get in touch with her when he goes to
　　　　　　　　　 聯　絡
　　　 New York.
　　　 （他到了紐約會和她聯絡。）

He has made up his mind to study hard.
　　= decided
(他已下決心要用功。)

Who takes charge of this class?
　　　　掌　理
= Who is in charge of this class?
(這個班由誰掌理？)

He'll │take care of│ my children when I go on
　　　 │look after │
a trip.
(我去旅行時，他會照顧我的小孩。)

Students have complete access to books in that
　　　　　　　　完全接觸
library.
(學生可以任意使用那座圖書館內的書。)

I look forward to seeing you soon.
(我期盼能很快見到你。)

１７．prefer (比較喜歡) 的用法：

a. prefer + │名詞　│ + to + │名詞　│
　　　　　　 │動名詞│　　介　 │動名詞│

例: I prefer coffee to tea.
　　(我比較喜歡喝咖啡，不喜歡喝茶。)

I prefer going to the movies to watching TV.
(我比較喜歡看電影，而非看電視。)

b. prefer to + 原形動詞 + │instead of + 動名詞　│
　　　　　　　　　　　　　 │rather than + 原形動詞│
　　　　　　　　　　　　　　　　連接詞

例: I prefer to go to the movies instead of
    watching TV.
  = I prefer to go to the movies rather than
    watch TV.
  = I prefer going to the movies to watching TV.
    I prefer to go to the movies rather than
    watching TV. (×)

18. mind (介意) 的用法:

　mind + if 子句
= mind + 動名詞

例: Would you mind if I opened the door?
    (Would 用過去式, if 子句之動詞亦用過去式)
    Do you mind if I open the door?
    (Do 爲現在式, 故 if 子句之動詞亦用現在式)
    (你介不介意我把門打開?)

    Would you mind if you came over here?
    Do you mind if you come over here?
    (你介不介意到這裡來?)

注意:
上列四句皆可化簡爲 mind + 動名詞, 法則如下:

a. 同主詞可省略, 若爲不同主詞, 則 if 子句之主詞變爲
   所有格;

b. if 子句之動詞變爲動名詞。

例:
                         my opening
    Would you mind ~~if I~~ opened the door?
    (不同主詞)
    (你介不介意我把門打開?)

opening

Would you mind ~~if you opened~~ the door?

（同主詞）

（你介不介意去把門打開？）

19. 動詞 ＋ 動名詞的結構：
下列動詞只能接動名詞，不能接不定詞。

*admit	承認	mention	提到
*avoid	避免	pardon	原諒
*appreciate	感激；體會	*miss	想念
*consider	考慮	*practise	練習
*delay	延期	=practice	
*mind	介意	*quit	停止
*deny	否認	risk	冒險
detest	憎恨	postpone	延遲
*enjoy	喜歡	*resent	憤恨
escape	逃避	*regret	後悔
excuse	原諒	*keep	保持
*finish	結束	*imagine	想像
forgive	原諒		

（註 * 表托福常考之動詞）

例: I really appreciate your helping me.
（我實在感謝你的幫助。）

He considered studying another language.
（他考慮學習另一種語言。）

He has finished writing this book.
（他已經寫完這本書。）

I enjoy talking with you.
（我喜歡和你談話。）

He practised to speak English every day. (×)

He practised speaking English every day. (○)
（他每天練習說英語。）

20. prevent one from + Ving　　禁止某人……
= forbid one to V

例: I prevented him from smoking.
= I forbade him to smoke.
I prevented him to smoke. (✕)
（我禁止他抽煙。）

注意:
動詞 + 受詞 + from 的結構尚有下列幾種:

　　to ban one from　　　禁止某人……
= to bar one from
= to prohibit one from
= to stop one from
= to keep one from
　　to save one from　　從……救出
　　to restrain one from　　限制某人

21. encourage one to + 原形動詞　　鼓勵某人去……

discourage one from + 動名詞　　阻止某人去……

例: I encouraged him to do it.
（我鼓勵他做此事。）

I discouraged him from coming here.
（我阻止他來這裡。）
I discouraged him to come here. (✕)

22. persuade one to + 原形動詞　　勸人去……

dissuade one from + 動名詞　　勸阻人……

例: I persuaded him to come with me.
= I prevailed on him to come with me.
= I talked him into coming with me.
（我勸服他和我一起來。）

I dissuaded him from coming with me.
I dissuaded him to come with me. (×)
（我勸他別跟我來。）

2 3．resemble + 受詞　　相似

例: You resemble your brother.
= You are like your brother.
（你很像你哥哥。）

You resemble to your brother. (×, to 應刪去)

You are resembling your brother.
（×,『相似』本身表持續狀態，故不可用進行式）

2 4．decide, determine（決心，決定）的用法:

a. decide 之後可接 (1) to V
　　　　　　　　 (2) on ┤ N
　　　　　　　　　　　　└ Ving
　　　　　　　　 (3) that 子句
　　　　　　　　 (4) N

例: I have decided to go to Paris for advanced
education.
（我決定到巴黎深造。）

After a long discussion, we have decided on
this plan.
（經過冗長的討論後，我們決定採行此計劃。）

He has decided on going to Paris for advanced
education.

= He has decided that he would go to Paris
for advanced education.

He has decided going to Paris. (×)
(他決定赴巴黎深造。)

The event decided his fate.
(這事件決定了他的命運。)

b. be determined to　　已下決心要……
determine to　　　　下決心要

例: I determined to go.
(我決心要走。)

I was determined to go.
(我已下決心要走。)

I determined going.
(×, determine 之後有動詞時, 應加 to + V)

I've determined the date of departure.
(我已決定離開的日期。)

2 5 . afford (花得起錢能買, 有能力做) 的用法

a. afford + 名詞

例: I can afford that car.
(我買得起那輛車。)

Since he has much money, he can afford a
new house.
(因為他錢多, 所以買得起新房子。)

　b. afford + to + 原形動詞

　　例: Since he has much money, he can afford to
　　　　buy a new house.

　　　　He cannot afford to go to school.
　　　　(他讀不起書。)
　　　　He cannot afford going to school. (×)

　c. afford　　提供
　 = provide

　　例: Going to school affords us knowledge.
　　　　(上學提供我們知識。)

26. wait for + 受詞　　等待
　= await + 受詞

　　例: I'll wait for you till three.
　　　= I'll await you till three.
　　　(我會等你到三點。)

　　　　I'll wait till three.
　　　(我會等到三點。)
　　　　I'll wait you till three. (×)
　　　　I'll await for you till three. (×)

　注意:
　wait on　　侍候
　= attend on

　　例: The servant doesn't like to wait on his master.
　　　　(該僕人不喜歡侍候他的主人。)

27. succeed, fail 的用法:

　a. succeed　 vi. 成功

succeed in | Ving
　　　　　　 | N

例: He succeeded after years of hard work.
　　(經年來的努力，他成功了。)

　　He succeeded in passing the test.
= He succeeded in the test.
　(他成功通過考試。)

　　He succeeded to pass the test.
　　(×，succeed 之後不能用不定詞)

b. succeed + 受詞　　vt. 繼承

例: He succeeded John as chairman of this committee.
　　(他繼承約翰為委員會之主席。)

c. fail　　vi. 失敗
fail to V

例: He failed in the test.
　= He failed to pass the test.
　　He failed in passing the test. (×)
　　(他考試沒過。)

d. fail　　vt. 使失敗; 無助於

例: Since John didn't study, his teacher failed him.
　　(由於約翰未用功，老師不讓他及格。)

28. depend, depend on 的用法:
depend 不加受詞表『依情形而定』。
depend on 加受詞表『依賴』。

例: I depend on him to give me advice.
　　　　　　受詞

(我靠他給我建議。)

I depend on it that he will come.
(我指望他會來。)
I depend on that he will come. (×)
(that 子句之前須加虛受詞 it)

A: "Can you come tomorrow?"
(你明天能來嗎？)

B: "That all depends on."
(×，depends on 之後應有受詞)

B: "That all depends." (○)
(那要看情形而定了。)

29. 感官動詞 look, feel, sound, taste, smell 其後只能加
形容詞，若要加名詞，要與 like 連用。

例: He looks happy.
(他看來很快樂。)
He looks like a happy man.

It tastes good.
(這嚐起來很好吃。)

It tastes like an apple.
(這嚐起來像蘋果。)

He looks happily. (×)

He looks a happy man. (×)

30.
try		設法
attempt		企圖
manage	+ to + 原形動詞	設法
endeavor		設法(含義較廣)

例：I'll try to study harder.
　　= I'll attempt to study harder.
　　= I'll manage to study harder.
　　　I'll manage at studying harder. (×)
　　（我要設法用功一點。）

　　　I'll endeavor to save our country.
　　（我將設法拯救國家。）

3 1. anger　vt. 使生氣
　　angry　adj. 生氣的

例：He angered me.
　　= I was angered by him.
　　（他使我生氣。）

　　　I was angered with him. (×)
　　　I'm angry with him. (對人用 with)
　　（我對他感到生氣。）
　　　I'm angry by him. (×)

　　　I'm angry at her attitude. (對事用 at)
　　= I am angered by her attitude.
　　（我對她的態度感到生氣。）

3 2. 授與動詞
　　授與動詞有兩個受詞，其公式有下列三種，所表達的意思則
　　完全相同：

　　a. 主詞 + 及物動詞 + 間接受詞（人）+ 直接受詞（物）

例：I gave him a book.
　　（我給他一本書。）

　　　He bought me a pencil.
　　（他為我買支鉛筆。）

He wrote me a letter.
(他寫封信給我。)

He taught me English.
(他教我英文。)

b. 主詞 + 及物動詞 + 直接受詞 + | to | + 間接受詞
　　　　　　　　　　(物)　　| for |　　(人)
　　　　　　　　　　　　　 | of |
　　　　　　　　　　　　　 | ： |
　　　　　　　　　　　　　 | ： |

例: I gave a book to him.

He bought a pencil for me.

He wrote a letter to me.

He taught English to me.

注意:
(1) 直接受詞 (物) + to + 間接受詞 (人)
give, send, lend, write, bring, deliver, show,
teach, tell, sell, pay。

例: I taught English to him.
(我教他英文。)

I paid thirty dollars to him.
(我付他三十元。)

(2) 直接受詞 (物) + for + 間接受詞 (人)
make, get, leave (留給), do, buy。

例: He made a chair for me.
(他為我做了張椅子。)

He bought a book for me.
（他爲我買了一本書。）

(3) 直接受詞（物）＋ of ＋ 間接受詞（人）
ask, expect, require, demand。

例: I asked a question of him.
（我向他問個問題。）

(4) 直接受詞（物）＋ on ＋ 間接受詞（人）

例: I played a joke on him.
（或 pulled）
（我開他一個玩笑。）

c. 被動用法:
主詞（人）＋ be ＋ 及物動詞 ＋ 受詞

例: He was given a book (by me).

I was bought a pencil (by him).

I was written a letter (by him).

I was taught English (by him).

3 3. 知覺動詞 ＋ 受詞 ＋ │ 原形動詞（表事實）
│ 現在分詞（表動作之進行）

a. 看: see, watch, notice, behold, look at。

例: I saw him go.
（我看到他走了。）

I saw him going.
（我看到他正在走。）

I watched him leaving.
（我注視著他正離去。）

b. 聽: listen to, hear。

例: I heard him talk.
（我聽到他說話。）

I heard him talking.
（我聽到他正在說話。）

c. 感覺: feel。

例: I felt him leave.
（我感覺他走了。）

I felt him leaving.
（我感覺他正在離去。）

3 4.
remember + to V	記得要……
remember + 動名詞	記得曾……
forget + to V	忘了要……
forget + 動名詞	忘了曾……
regret + to V	抱歉要……
regret + 動名詞	後悔曾……

例: I'll remember to see him.
（我會記得要去看他。）

I remembered to see him.
（我記得要去看他的。）

I remember seeing him before.
（我記得曾經看過他。）

I forgot to see him.
(我忘了要去看他。)

I forgot seeing him before.
(我忘了曾經見過他。)

I regret to tell you the truth.
(我抱歉要告訴你眞相。)

I regret telling you the truth.
(我後悔曾告訴你眞相。)

Exercise

Ⅰ. 請選出一個正確的答案:

1 . Rose went to the party, although she _____.
   (A) was knowing she would not like it
   (B) knew she was not liking it
   (C) knew she would not like it
   (D) was knowing she did not like it

2 . Novelist Edna Ferber _____ her youth in Appleton, Wisconsin.
   (A) spending (B) was spent (C) spent (D) who spent

3 . Of the two houses, the family preferred _____.
   (A) the one in a more isolation
   (B) the more isolated one
   (C) one being in more isolation
   (D) one that is more isolated

4 . I came to lunch so early because I thought the bell had already _____.
   (A) rang (B) ring (C) been rang (D) rung

5 . You _____ your visa extended before it expires.
   (A) had better to get   (B) had to get better
   (C) had better get   (D) had better got

6 . The health program outlined in the article seems very sound to me, but it has _____ considerable public outcry.
   (A) met with   (B) met up with
   (C) run up with   (D) run against

7 . My typist has not returned my paper yet, but she
    promised _____ by tomorrow.
    (A) for me to have it ready
    (B) it was ready for me
    (C) me it was ready
    (D) to have it ready for me

8 . Al said that he wouldn't mind _____.
    (A) to wait for us   (B) wait for us
    (C) waiting for us   (D) waiting us

9 . She said that she would rather not _____ it right now.
    (A) discussing   (B) to discuss
    (C) discuss   (D) discussion

1 0 . Anna said in her letter that she'd appreciate _____
    from you some time.
    (A) to hear   (B) having heard
    (C) hearing   (D) to hearing

1 1 . I have a letter from your uncle. Do you object _____ it?
    (A) to my reading   (B) that I read
    (C) from my reading   (D) to I read

1 2 . Our city has changed a great deal. It doesn't even
    resemble_____.
    (A) the one of three years ago
    (B) one three years ago
    (C) the one since three years
    (D) one from three years

1 3 . Uncle Dick has already arrived. Do you expect _____
    to see him?
    (A) going (B) go (C) to go (D) that you go

14. Scientists continue to speculate _____ causes sunspots.
    (A) for what   (B) what about
    (C) whatever   (D) about what

15. Ann doesn't like milk. She says that she never _____
    it at home.
    (A) use to drinking   (B) used to drinking
    (C) used to drink   (D) use to drink

16. Edward likes classical music and I think that he
    prefers it _____ any other kind.
    (A) than   (B) over   (C) to   (D) against

17. Would you please _____ the listening comprehension
    script until after you have listened to the tape.
    (A) not to read   (B) not read
    (C) don't read   (D) don't to read

18. Greater efforts to increase wheat production must
    be made if bread shortages _____ avoided.
    (A) will be (B) can be (C) are to be (D) were to be

19. It's not too cloudy to take a picture. I think it
    _____.
    (A) is quite enough light   (B) has enough light
    (C) is light enough   (D) has very light enough

20. The future price of gold _____ by a number of inter-
    related factors.
    (A) is going to determine   (B) will determine
    (C) will be determine   (D) will be determined

21. Mr. Bundy is so strange today. And your manners
    _____ , too.
    (A) like this is   (B) are like his

(C) like he is　　　　　　(D) like him are

2 2 . I want to go to the dentist, but you _____ with me.
(A) need not to go　　　　(B) do not need go
(C) need not go　　　　　(D) need go not

2 3 . Dr. Samuels became a politician because he wanted
to _____.
(A) make his society changed
(B) bring about changes in his society
(C) bring about a changed society
(D) result in new changes for his society

2 4 . I bite my nails. I must break _____.
(A) the habit to me　　　　(B) the habit with myself
(C) myself of the habit　　(D) of the habit myself

2 5 . You don't object _____ you by your first name, do
you?
(A) that I call　　　　　　(B) to my calling
(C) for calling　　　　　　(D) that I am call

2 6 . I'm not going to ask the teacher why he gave me that
grade; I intend _____.
(A) to let rest the matter
(B) the matter to be let resting
(C) letting the matter to rest
(D) to let the matter rest

2 7 . Tanbark was spread on the streets to _____ of traffic
when Mrs. Campbell was appearing on the stage.
(A) lessen the sound　　　(B) deaden the noise
(C) decrease the voices　　(D) take away the noise

2 8 . What did he say in the letter? I really can't _____
it out.

(A) make　(B) put　(C) run　(D) come

2 9. I am sorry I lost the race, but I really wasn't fast
enough to catch _____ the other runners.
(A) up　(B) up with　(C) to　(D) with

3 0. How will it turn out? Well, it all _____.
(A) depends on　　　　　(B) is depending
(C) depends　　　　　　(D) depend

Ⅱ. 請選出錯誤的劃線部份：

3 1. One of the workers <u>has</u> <u>hung</u> the curtains that <u>had</u>
　　　　　　　　　　　A　　B　　　　　　　　　　　　C

been <u>laying</u> on the floor.
　　　D

3 2. Although his lawyer felt <u>very</u> <u>badly</u> about the
　　　　　　　　　　　　　　A　　B

verdict, he <u>advised</u> him <u>not to appeal</u> the case.
　　　　　　　C　　　　　　D

3 3. The landlady <u>suspicioned</u> that someone <u>must</u> have
　　　　　　　　A　　　　　　　　　　　　B

broken <u>into</u> the house while she <u>was watching</u>
　　　　C　　　　　　　　　　　　　D

the TV show.

3 4. <u>Because of</u> the accident, Grandmother will forbid my
　　A

brother and <u>me</u> <u>from swimming</u> in the river unless
　　　　　B　　　C

someone <u>agrees</u> to watch us.
　　　　D

３５. Ellen <u>would prefer</u> <u>going</u> to the theater more
　　　　　　 A 　　　　　　 B

　　 frequently, but her schedule <u>prevents</u> her
　　　　　　　　　　　　　　　　　　　　　 C

　　 <u>attending</u> at more than one play a month.
　　　 D

標準答案：1.(C)　2.(C)　3.(B)　4.(D)　5.(C)　6.(A)　7.(D)
　　　　　　 8.(C)　9.(C)　10.(C)　11.(A)　12.(A)　13.(C)　14.(D)
　　　　　　 15.(C)　16.(C)　17.(B)　18.(C)　19.(B)　20.(D)　21.(B)
　　　　　　 22.(C)　23.(B)　24.(C)　25.(B)　26.(D)　27.(B)　28.(A)
　　　　　　 29.(B)　30.(C)　31.(D)　32.(B)　33.(A)　34.(C)　35.(D)

習題解答：

　1. know, like（喜歡）等字爲瞬間即知的動詞（即頃刻間即可了
　　　解自己是否喜歡、討厭、知道、明白等動詞），不可能用進行式。

　2. 主詞 Novelist Edna Ferber 之後應接過去式及物動詞 spent。

　3. (B) 是最好的答案，因名詞避免重複，故用 one 代替 house，
　　　同時前有定冠詞限定兩個房子之一。

　4. had 之後用過去分詞 rung（原式 ring，過去式 rang）。

　5. had better 爲助動詞，故其後用原形動詞 get。

　6. meet with = encounter　　遭遇到

　7. promise（答應，允諾）之用法：
　　　promise + to V
　　　promise + 受詞 + to V
　　　promise + that 子句
　　　例：He promised to come with me.
　　　　 （他答應跟我來。）
　　　　　 He promised me to come here by 6.

(他答應我六點鐘之前要來。)
He promised (me) that he would come here by 6.
(他答應六點鐘之前要來。)

8. mind + Ving   在意……
   wait for   等待……

9. would rather not + 原形動詞   寧願不……

10. appreciate + Ving   感激
(B)雖爲動名詞,但 she'd appreciate...= she would
appreciate..., 時態上是表示『未來』,故不能用表完
成之 having heard。

11. 表『反對』的動詞如下:
I object to going to the movies with him.
        介
=I oppose going to the movies with him.
=I am opposed to going to the movies with him.
           介
(我反對和他去看電影。)

12. the one = the city, 係限定用法, 故 one 之前應加 the。

13. expect 的用法:
I expect to go on a trip this summer.
(我盼望今夏去旅行。)
I expect you to go on a trip this summer.
(我指望你今年夏天去旅行。)
I expect much of you.
(我對你期望很高。)
I expect some changes in the plan.
(我預期該項計劃將有所改變。)

14. speculate about   深思,思慮
= speculate on

15. used to + V　　過去習慣於……
    be used to Ving　　現在習慣於……

16. prefer A to B　　喜歡 A 勝於 B

17. please 若表『請』，視為副詞，其後跟原形動詞：
    肯定句：Please come here at 8.
    　　　　　Please to come here at 8.(×)
    　　　　　（請你八點來。）
    否定句：Please don't make noise.
    　　　　　Please not make noise.(×)
    　　　　　（請不要發出噪音。）
    慣用語：Would you please + 原形動詞　　請你……好嗎？

    例：Would you please open the door?
    　　Would you please not open the door?
    　　Would you please not to open the door? (×)

18. be to 可表『預定，義務，可能』。
    (1) 表預定 = be expected to
       例：He is to be here by nine this evening.
       　　（預定他今晚九時前來此地。）
    (2) 表義務 = must
       例：He is to finish all the work before he can leave.
       　　（= must）
       　　（他必須在走之前完成所有的工作。）
    (3) 表可能 = is likely to
       例：It is to rain today.
       　　（很可能今天會下雨。）
    本題之 is to = must。

19. 此處的 light 為名詞，故 enough 為形容詞，應放在所修飾
    的名詞之前。

20. determine 為及物動詞，其後應有受詞，否則須用被動語態。

19. 此處的 light 爲名詞，故 enough 爲形容詞，應放在所修飾
　　的名詞之前。

20. determine 爲及物動詞，其後應有受詞，否則須用被動語態。

例: He determined the policy.
   = The policy was determined by him.

2 1 . And your manners are like his (manners), too.
(你的態度也像他的態度。)

2 2 . need not 爲助動詞，之後要加原形動詞。
(B) 應改爲 do not need to go。

2 3 . change 可作不及物動詞和及物動詞，但意義不同。

例: He has changed a lot since he came here.
       不及物動詞
   (自從他來這兒之後，人變了許多。——他還是人，
   只是氣質變了。)
   He has been changed a lot since he came here.
           及物動詞
   (自從他來這兒之後，他被改變了許多。——很可能他被改
   變成另一種東西，而非人。)
是故如用 (A) 的話，則 make his society changed 暗示
make his society changed (into something else)，因
此是錯的，應改爲 make his society change (不及物動
詞)，即社會還是社會，只是有些地方有所改變。
(B) 是對的。...bring about 此處等於 promote (促成)。
(C) bring about a changed society (促成一個改變的社
    會) 暗示在已存在的社會中，再帶來一個已改變的社會，
    是故語意錯誤。
(D) result in (導致) 之主詞不能是『人』，而是『原因』。

    例: His carelessness resulted in this accident.
        原因   =caused
                        =brought about
                        =led to
                        =culminated in
    但 bring about 的主詞可爲『人』亦可爲『原因』。

例: He brought about this accident.
　　(他促使此次車禍的發生。)
　　 His carelessness brought about this accident.
　　(他的粗心導致了此次車禍的發生。)

2 4. break｜oneself of...　　戒除……
　　　rid

2 5. 請見第11題解答。

2 6. intend to + V = intend + Ving
　　例: I intend to leave today.
　　　=I intend leaving today.
　　　(我打算今天離開。)

2 7. deaden 使(聲音)漸消
　　lessen 減少(數量)
　　decrease 減少(產量)
　　take away 拿走(實物)

2 8. make it out 理解
　　put it out 滅火
　　come out (of)　　(從……)走出來
　　run out (不及物動詞片語)用光
　　例: He ran out of money.
　　　(他錢花光了。)

2 9. catch up with　　趕上
　　例: Run faster, or he will catch up with you.
　　　(跑快一點,否則他會趕上你。)

3 0. depends 之後若有受詞,應加 on,此處無受詞,故不加 on。

3 1. (D) laying 應改為 lying,因其後無受詞,故用不及物動詞
　　lie 之現在分詞形態,表進行的動作。

32. badly 應改爲 bad, 因感官動詞之後只能加形容詞。

33. (A) 應改爲動詞 suspected, 因 suspicion 作名詞用。

34. (C) 應改爲 to swim。
    forbid...to + 原形動詞　　不許……去……

35. (D) 應改爲 from attending at。
    prevent...from Ving　　使……無法……

第六章
時態及語態

概說:

　　記得以前唸初中(現稱爲國中)的時候，每次上英文課，就提不起興趣，主要是因爲鄉下的孩子比較保守，不敢跟著老師大聲唸，尤其有些英文字唸起來頗像閩南語中的髒字，如 goodbye(牛的生殖器)；morning (摸乳)。每每在親朋好友面前『秀』一兩個英文字，就會被回罵一聲『夭壽』，害得我一直不敢開口說英語。及至老師教到時態時，就被那些複雜(當時覺得)的規則嚇壞了，從此再也不唸英文了。

　　十八歲之後，發誓要把英文唸好時，我就強迫自己每天一定看十六個小時的英文。我的方法無他，就是勤背誦、勤查字典。不知不覺中，文章愈來愈看得懂。但練習寫作時，就發現自己最大的毛病乃時態運用不當，頻頻出錯。於是，我就買了一本虹橋書局出版的英文版 Mastering American English。這本文法書用淺顯的例句，把時態變化交待得很清楚。從此，我如魚得水。閱讀文章時，就特別注意時態的用法，久而久之，便習慣其中用法，而且我也不必再看任何文法參考書了。

　　說了那麼多話，無非希望同學明白，學英語，一如學其他外語，急不得也。有道是『慢工出細活。』希望同學一方面細看『常春藤英文文法』，一方面多看英文文章，以印證雄哥在書中所說的重點。長此以後，你的英文一定與我的一樣好，甚至超越我。耐心地努力下去吧！

第一節　時態

1．時態的種類

　　a．簡單式：
　　　(1) 現在式：He <u>writes</u> a letter everyday.
　　　　　　　　(他每天寫信。)

(2) 過去式：He <u>wrote</u> a letter yesterday.
　　　　　　　（他昨天寫一封信。）

(3) 未來式：He <u>will write</u> a letter tomorrow.
　　　　　　　（他明天要寫一封信。）

b. 完成式：
　(1) 現在完成式：He <u>has written</u> a letter.
　　　　　　　　　（他已經寫好一封信。）

　(2) 過去完成式：He <u>had written</u> a letter when I came.
　　　　　　　　　（我回來時他早就寫好一封信。）

　(3) 未來完成式：He <u>will have written</u> a letter before
　　　　　　　　　I come.
　　　　　　　　　（我回來之前，他將會寫好一封信。）

c. 進行式：
　(1) 現在進行式：He <u>is writing</u> a letter now.
　　　　　　　　　（他現在正在寫信。）

　(2) 過去進行式：He <u>was writing</u> a letter when I came.
　　　　　　　　　（我來時，他正在寫信。）

　(3) 未來進行式：He <u>will be writing</u> a letter when I
　　　　　　　　　come.
　　　　　　　　　（我來時，他將正在寫信。）

d. 完成進行式：
　(1) 現在完成進行式：He <u>has been writing</u> a letter
　　　　　　　　　　　for two hours.
　　　　　　　　　　　（他已經寫信寫兩小時。）

　(2) 過去完成進行式：He <u>had been writing</u> a letter
　　　　　　　　　　　for two hours.
　　　　　　　　　　　（他當時早已經寫信寫兩小時。）

2. 使用現在式的時機

　a. 表知覺、狀態、所有:

　　例: I smell something burning.
　　　(我聞到東西燒焦的味道。)

　　　You look worried.
　　　(你看起來愁眉苦臉。)

　　　This medicine tastes bitter to me.
　　　(對我而言, 這個藥很苦。)

　　　He has a book.
　　　(他有一本書。)

　　　Your hands feel cold.
　　　(你的手很冰冷。)

　　　He is a student.
　　　(他是學生。)

　　　I see a man standing there.
　　　(我看到一個人站在那裡。)

　b. 表習慣性的動作:

　　例: He goes to school everyday.
　　　(他每天上學。)

　　　He writes a letter everyday.
　　　(他每天寫信。)

　　　He always takes a bus home.
　　　(他總是搭公車回家。)

注意:
表習慣性的動作常以時間副詞修飾。

例: It rains a lot <u>in summer</u>.
(夏天雨量大。)

They <u>seldom</u> take a trip.
(他們很少去旅行。)

千萬不可造這種句子:
He writes a letter. (劣)
(他寫信。)

He comes back. (劣)
(他回來。)

因這兩個例子無時間副詞修飾, 故不是習慣性的動作,
因此無意義。

c. 表真理、事實、格言:

例: The sun rises in the east.
(太陽從東方昇起。)

He who is lazy is doomed to failure.
(凡是懶惰的人註定要失敗。)

Honesty is the best policy.
(誠實是上策。)

d. 表未來:

begin, start, arrive, leave, come, go 等動詞可用現
在式表未來。

例: They arrive tomorrow.

（他們明天到。）

It begins at 7.
（七點開始。）

They start the day after tomorrow.
（他們後天出發。）

Does he come tomorrow?
（他明天要來嗎？）

3. 使用過去式的時機

　　a. 表過去的動作、習慣、狀態：

　　例：I saw him yesterday.
　　（我昨天看到他。）

He always rose early in the morning.
（他從前都很早起床。）

He was born in 1970.
（他生於一九七○年。）

　　b. 表過去的經驗(亦可用現在完成式表示)：

Did you ever see her before?
= Have you ever seen her before?
（你見過她嗎？）

　　c. 句中若有 after, until, before 等連接詞引導的子句，由於時間先後很清楚，可用過去式代替過去完成式。

　　例：After I <u>had finished</u> the work, I went home.
　　= After I <u>finished</u> the work, I went home.
　　（我完成工作之後就回家。）

I <u>had not studied</u> English until I was 10.
= I <u>didn't study</u> English until I was 10.
(我十歲開始學英文。)

Before I came here, I <u>had lived</u> in Japan for
a long time.
= Before I came here, I <u>lived</u> in Japan for a
long time.
(我來這裡之前曾在日本住過很長一段時間。)

4. 使用未來式的時機
表未來發生的動作或狀態:

例: It will rain tomorrow.
(明天會下雨。)

He will be a student soon.
(他很快就是學生了。)

Will you be able to come?
(你能來嗎?)

注意:

a. 表未來或條件的副詞子句一定要用現在式, 而主要子句用
未來式。

例: When I <u>have</u> money, I <u>will</u> buy a car.
(我有錢的時候就要買車。)

I <u>won't</u> buy a car unless I <u>have</u> money.
(除非我有錢否則我不買車。)

When I <u>will have</u> money, I will buy a
car. (✕)

b. be going to = will

例: He is going to come.
= He will come.
(他將要來。)

5. 使用現在完成式的時機

a. 表到現在為止完成的動作:

例: I have just finished my homework.
(我剛做完功課。)

She has already come.
(她已經來了。)

He has gone to New York.
(他已到紐約去了。——人在紐約)

He hasn't gone to work yet.
(他還沒去工作。)

b. 表到現在為止的經驗:

例: I have met him several times.
(我見過他幾次。)

I have never met such a man as he.
(我從未見過像他這樣的人。)

c. 表到現在為止仍在繼續的動作或狀態:

例: She has lived here for 10 years.
(And she still lives here.)
(她已經在這裡住十年了。——她仍然住在這裡。)

She has studied English since 1967.
(And she still studies English.)

（她從一九六七年就開始學英文。——她現在還在學。）

注意：
表『曾來過』『曾去過』等經驗時，用 "have been"，而
非 "have gone" 或 "have come"。

例：He has gone to Hongkong. （他已經到香港去了。）
　　（And he is now in Hongkong.）（他現在在香港。）

　　He has been to Hongkong.
　= He has gone to Hongkong and come back again.
　　（他曾去過香港。）

6. 使用過去完成式的時機
　　表截至過去某時爲止所完成的動作、經驗：

例：He had studied English for 10 years before he left
　　for the States.
　　（他赴美之前已學過十年英文。）

　　He had already left when I came.
　　（我來時他已離開了。）

　　He was angry because he hadn't seen Mary.
　　（他沒看到瑪麗，因此生氣。）

　　He told me that he had seen the movie once.
　　（他告訴我，這部電影他已看過一次。）

注意：
過去完成式不能單獨存在，要與另一過去式子句或表過去之副
詞片語連用，即在過去不同時間發生的兩種動作：

先發生的 —→ 用過去完成式
後發生的 —→ 用簡單過去式

例: I lost the book which my father had given me.
(我弄丟了父親給我的書。)

My father <u>had given</u> me a book and I lost it.
(×，過去完成式不能單獨存在。)

但連接詞用 and 時，則兩個子句均用過去式。

例: My father gave me a book and I lost it.

7. 使用未來完成式的時機
表到未來某時為止所完成或仍在繼續的動作或經驗等:

例: He will have arrived in Chicago by this time
tomorrow.
(明天這個時候，他將已抵達芝加哥。)

When you come (或 By the time you come),
everything will have been finished.
(你來的時候每一件事將已全部完成。)

He will have lived here for 10 years by the end
of this month.
(到月底，他就在此地住滿十年了。)

8. 使用現在進行式的時機

a. 表現在正在做的動作:

例: He is writing a letter.
(他正在寫一封信。)

What are you doing?
(你正在做什麼?)

He is taking a trip now.

（他現在正在旅遊。）

Many girls are dancing over there.
（許多女孩正在那裡跳舞。）

b. 表即將發生的動作，常與表未來的副詞並用：

He is coming today.
= He will be coming today.
（他即將於今天前來。）

He is leaving soon.
= He will be leaving soon.
（他很快就要離開。）

9. 使用過去進行式的時機

a. 表過去某時正在做的動作：

He was studying English then.
（那時他正在讀英文。）

He was taking a bath when you called.
（你打電話來的時候，他正在洗澡。）

注意：
was going to　　　本擬……
= was about to

例：He was going to commit suicide, but I
　　stopped him.
= He was about to commit suicide, but I
　　stopped him.
（他本想要自殺的，但我阻止了他。）

b. 表過去式中即將發生的事：

例: He was dying.
  = He was to die.
  = He was about to die.
  (那時他快死了。)

10. 使用未來進行式的時機
  用以表示於未來某時將進行的動作:

例: He will be studying English at this time tomorrow.
  (明天此時,他將正在研讀英文。)

11. 使用現在完成進行式的時機
  表一直繼續到現在且仍將繼續下去的動作:

例: She has been working with this company for
  5 years.
  (她在這家公司服務已有五年的時間。——也許還要服務
  下去。)

  They have been standing here since 7 this morning.
  (他們從早上七點就一直站在這兒。——現在還在站。)

  He has been teaching at this school since 1976.
  (他從一九七六年就一直在這個學校任教。——他還要繼
  續教。)

12. 使用過去完成進行式的時機
  表一直繼續到過去某時,而當時仍在繼續進行的動作:

例: I had been sleeping when he came.
  (他來的時候,我仍在睡覺。)

  He told us that he had been studying German since
  1960.
  (他告訴我們他從1960年起就一直學德文。)

13. 使用未來完成進行式的時機
    表一直繼續到未來某時，而仍將繼續進行的動作：

    例: I will have been teaching English for ten
        years by the end of this year.
        (到今年年底，我教英文將已有十年了。)

14. 時態的前後一致

    a. 主要子句為現在式，從屬子句除過去完成式，過去完成進
       行式不能用以外，其他時態皆可用。

       例: I think | he has come.
                   | he is coming.
                   | he already came.
                   | he will have come by the end of
                   | this month.
                   | he was singing a song when I came
                   | yesterday.
                   | he had come. (✕)
                   | he had been sleeping. (✕)
                   | he had been sleeping when I came.(○,
                   因有過去式之副詞子句 when I came)

    b. 主要子句為過去式時，則子句不得用表現在或未來的時態
       ，但可使用過去式、過去完成式、過去進行式、過去完成
       進行式。

       例: I thought | he was nice.
                     | he had come back.
                     | he would come back.
                     | he was working hard.
                     | he had been working hard.
                     | he will come back. (✕)
                     | he has been working hard. (✕)

c. 子句表眞理時，無論主要子句是過去、現在或未來式，該子句都用現在式。

例: They <u>knew</u> that the sun <u>rises</u> in the east.
（他們知道太陽從東邊昇起。）

We <u>know</u> that the sun <u>rises</u> in the east.
（我們知道太陽從東邊昇起。）

She <u>will know</u> that the sun <u>rises</u> in the east.
（她將會知道太陽從東方昇起。）

15. | for
during
in
through
down through
over | the | past
last | (10) years

這些片語多與現在完成式或現在完成進行式並用。

例: I have been studying English for the past week.
（一個星期來，我都一直在唸英文。）

16. It is + 時間 + since...　　自從……
= It has been + 時間 + since...

例: It has been five years since I saw you last time.
= It is five years since I saw you last time.
（從我上次見到你，至今已有五年了。）

17. 常用的不規則動詞變化

a. A－A－A型 （三式相同）

原　式	過去式	過去分詞	
burst	burst	burst	突發
cost	cost	cost	值，花費
cast	cast	cast	丟，擲
cut	cut	cut	切
hit	hit	hit	擊
hurt	hurt	hurt	傷害
let	let	let	讓
read	read	read	讀
set	set	set	置，放
shut	shut	shut	關
upset	upset	upset	使……難過

b. **Ａ－Ｂ－Ｂ型** （過去式與過去分詞同形）

say	said	said	說
lay	laid	laid	置，生蛋
pay	paid	paid	付款
sell	sold	sold	賣
tell	told	told	告訴
catch	caught	caught	捕
teach	taught	taught	教
buy	bought	bought	買
bring	brought	brought	帶來
think	thought	thought	想
have / has	had	had	有，使，吃，喝，經歷
hear	heard	heard	聽
make	made	made	做
build	built	built	建造
lend	lent	lent	借給，貸
send	sent	sent	寄，送
spend	spent	spent	花費，度(時)
sit	sat	sat	坐
get	got	got	得
lose	lost	lost	失去，輸
win	won	won	贏得

smell	smelt	smelt	聞，嗅
hold	held	held	握
meet	met	met	遇見
feed	fed	fed	飼，餵
feel	felt	felt	感覺
keep	kept	kept	保持
sleep	slept	slept	睡
lead	led	led	領導
leave	left	left	離開
mean	meant	meant	意指
stand	stood	stood	站立，忍受
understand	understood	understood	了解
find	found	found	發現
hang	hung	hung	掛，吊
strike	struck	struck stricken	打擊

c.　A－B－A型　（現在式與過去分詞同形）

run	ran	run	跑
come	came	come	來
become	became	become	成爲

d.　A－B－C型　（三式不同形）

begin	began	begun	開始
drink	drank	drunk	喝
ring	rang	rung	搖鈴，鳴響
sing	sang	sung	唱
sink	sank	sunk	沈
swim	swam	swum	游泳
break	broke	broken	破
speak	spoke	spoken	說話
steal	stole	stolen	偷
freeze	froze	frozen	冰凍
choose	chose	chosen	選擇
hide	hid	hidden	藏
bite	bit	bitten	咬

tear	tore	torn	撕
wear	wore	worn	穿，戴
drive	drove	driven	駕
ride	rode	ridden	騎
rise	rose	risen	升
write	wrote	written	寫
take	took	taken	取
mistake	mistook	mistaken	誤會
shake	shook	shaken	搖動
know	knew	known	知道，認識
grow	grew	grown	生長
throw	threw	thrown	投
draw	drew	drawn	畫，拉
fly	flew	flown	飛
blow	blew	blown	吹
do	did	done	做
eat	ate	eaten	吃
fall	fell	fallen	落
give	gave	given	給
go	went	gone	去
lie	lay	lain	躺，臥
see	saw	seen	看
show	showed	shown	顯示
forget	forgot	forgotten	忘記

原式（現在式）

	am, is	was	
be		been	是，在
	are	were	

e. 有兩種活用變化的動詞

	burned	burned	燃燒
burn			
	burnt	burnt	

dream	dreamed	dreamed	夢見
	dreamt	dreamt	
learn	learned	learned	學習
	learnt	learnt	
spell	spelled	spelled	拼字
	spelt	spelt	

f．A－B－型　（變化不完全的助動詞）

現在式	過去式	過去分詞
shall	should	
will	would	
can	could	
may	might	

第二節　語態

1 . 語態的動詞一定是及物動詞

主動語態: I love him.

被動語態: He is loved by me.

注意:
不及物動詞只有主動語態，而無被動語態

例: I lay on the desk. (不及物)
→ On the desk was lain by me. (×)
(我躺在桌子上。)

I laid a book on the desk. (及物)
→ A book was laid on the desk by me. (○)
(書本被我放在桌上。)

2 . 原句的受詞作主詞 + be + 過去分詞 = 被動語態

例:
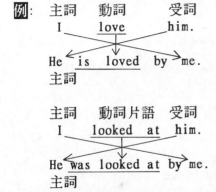

主詞　　動詞　　　受詞
　I　　　love　　　him.

He　is　loved　by　me.
主詞

主詞　　動詞片語　受詞
　I　　　looked at　him.

He was looked at by me.
主詞

```
      主詞      動詞片語        受詞
      I will take care of him.
```

```
      He will be taken care of by me.
      主詞
```

時\語態\態		主　動　語　態	被　動　語　態
簡單式	現在	He does it.	It is done by him.
	過去	He did it.	It was done by him.
	未來	He will do it.	It will be done by him.
完成式	現在	He has done it.	It has been done by him.
	過去	He had done it.	It had been done by him.
	未來	He will have done it.	It will have been done by him.
進行式	現在	He is doing it.	It is being done by him.
	過去	He was doing it.	It was being done by him.
	未來	He will be doing it.	[缺]

3 . 主動語態和被動語態時態要一致

例: I love him.
　= He is loved by me.
　（我愛他。）

　　I loved him.
　= He was loved by me.
　　（我以前愛他。）

　　I will love him.
　= He will be loved by me.

（我將會愛他。）

He is doing that work.
= That work is being done by him.
（他正在做那工作。）

4．授與動詞有兩種被動語態

例: I gave him a book.
= He was given a book by me.
= A book was given (to) him by me.
（我給他一本書。）

I taught him English.
= He was taught English by me.
= English was taught (to) him by me.
（我教他英文。）

5．動詞 + 介詞 + 受詞時，要把動詞 + 介詞視爲及物動詞，
可變被動語態

例: I live in this house.
= This house is lived in by me.
This house is lived by me. （×）
（我住在這個房子裡。）

I paid attention to him.
= He was paid attention to by me.
He was paid attention by me. （×）
（我注意著他。）

6．否定句的語態變化

例: They do not love him.
= He is not loved by them.
（他們不愛他。）

Exercise

I . 請選出一個正確的答案:

1 . The Government _____ employ wide surveillance but the
Department of Justice objected to it.
(A) is about to   (B) was about to
(C) in order to   (D) ought to

2 . The United States _____ to build a supersonic
aircraft but there was no support for it in the
Congress.
(A) has intended   (B) is intended
(C) had intended   (D) is intending

3 . There's a police car in front of our neighbor's
house.
What do you suppose _____ ?
(A) is happened   (B) has happened
(C) would happen   (D) did happen

4 . I came so early for lunch today because I thought
the bell _____ .
(A) had already rang   (B) has already rung
(C) already had rung   (D) had already rung

5 . James has just arrived, but I didn't know he _____
until yesterday.
(A) will come   (B) was coming
(C) had been coming   (D) comes

6 . The streets are all wet. It _____ during the night.
(A) must be raining   (B) must have been rain
(C) had to rain   (D) must have rained

7. I will go home for vacation as soon as I _____ my exams.
   (A) will finish   (B) finish
   (C) am finishing   (D) finished

8. Martin visited his aunt two days before he _____ town.
   (A) left   (B) will leave
   (C) had left   (D) is going to leave

9. As yet we _____ nothing from my brother.
   (A) did not hear   (B) had not heard
   (C) has heard   (D) have heard

10. I _____ to Taipei before I entered this school.
    (A) once gone   (B) have once gone
    (C) had once gone   (D) had once been

11. The commander-in-chief _____ the Pacific Ocean when the telegram reaches him.
    (A) will cross   (B) will be crossing
    (C) has crossed   (D) had crossed

12. The whole area was flooded because it _____ for weeks.
    (A) rains   (B) has rained
    (C) had been raining   (D) was raining

13. Our sales _____ for months, so we are now in great financial difficulty.
    (A) have been dropping   (B) had been dropping
    (C) have been dropped   (D) are dropping

14. I will lend you the book when I _____ with it.
    (A) do   (B) have done
    (C) am doing   (D) shall do

15. The moment I _____ the news, I turned pale.
 (A) have heard (B) hear
 (C) heard (D) was hearing

16. While I _____ with my wife last night, an old friend
 of mine showed up.
 (A) was talking (B) had talked
 (C) talked (D) would talk

17. We will wait right here until David _____ back.
 (A) has got (B) will have got
 (C) gets (D) get

18. We have been told the final outcome of the negotiations,
 but we shall never know what _____ on behind the scenes.
 (A) goes (B) went
 (C) had gone (D) will have been going

19. The clock has been working well since he _____ it for me.
 (A) has fixed (B) had fixed
 (C) fixed (D) would fix

20. Joseph _____ Hongkong by the end of this month.
 (A) will have reached (B) has reached
 (C) reaches (D) is reaching

Ⅱ. 選出錯誤的劃線部份

21. She thought that she <u>will</u> have <u>to wait</u> in line
                 A   B
 because <u>there were</u> <u>many people</u> in the office.
            C   D

22. It is possible that Indians originally <u>have migrated</u>
                                      A

to the Western Hemisphere <u>over</u> a bridge of land that
                                     B

<u>once existed</u> <u>between</u> Siberia and Alaska.
    C   D

23. <u>When</u> Harry Truman <u>has become</u> the President of the
    A   B
United States <u>he was</u> not familiar with <u>either</u> the
              C   D
foreign policy or the atomic bomb.

24. He <u>has been sitting</u> at the table for several hours
         A
and <u>drank</u> <u>considerably</u> more wine <u>than is</u> good for
     B   C   D
his health.

25. <u>Before</u> he died, the old man who <u>lives</u> next door to
   A   B
the drugstore used <u>to feed</u> the pigeons <u>three times</u>
               C   D
a day.

26. Medical researchers have <u>not yet</u> been able <u>to have</u>
                      A   B
<u>developed</u> an <u>effective</u> vaccine <u>against</u> influenza.
   C   D

27. Learning <u>a foreign</u> language is especially difficult
          A
for those <u>who</u> <u>had never learned</u> <u>one</u> before.
        B   C   D

28. Unfortunately, <u>two of the</u> boys <u>has been bit</u> by snakes
              A   B
the <u>last time</u> the family camped <u>in</u> the valley.
    C   D

29. To Mrs. Foster and Miss Rosen the advice sounded
    <u>wrong</u>, but everyone <u>else</u> at the meeting <u>consider</u> it
    　A　　　　　　　　　　　B　　　　　　　　　　　C
    <u>perfect</u>.
    　D

30. <u>In all</u> the years that Paul and I <u>have been</u> friends,
    　A　　　　　　　　　　　　　　　　　B
    I never <u>knew</u> him friendly to <u>anyone else</u>.
    　　　　C　　　　　　　　　　　D

標準答案： 1.(B)　2.(C)　3.(B)　4.(D)　5.(B)　6.(D)　7.(B)
　　　　　 8.(A)　9.(D)　10.(D)　11.(B)　12.(C)　13.(A)　14.(B)
　　　　　 15.(C)　16.(A)　17.(C)　18.(B)　19.(C)　20.(A)　21.(A)
　　　　　 22.(A)　23.(B)　24.(B)　25.(B)　26.(B)　27.(C)　28.(B)
　　　　　 29.(C)　30.(C)

習題講解：

1. a. but 之後的子句中動詞 objected to 係過去式，因此不可
      能選(A)。
   b. was about to = was going to 正要
   c. (C)非動詞
   d. (D) ought to 不能用在過去式，只用在現在或未來。
         例: He ought to go now.
             He ought to go tomorrow.
         ought to 若表過去時，應加 have 形成假設
         語氣，表與過去相反的事實。
         例: He ought to have gone yesterday.
             (But he didn't go.)

2. but 之後子句中動詞為過去式 there was...，故前面的子句
   也要用過去式。
      I had intended to go, but I had no money.
   = I intended to have gone, but I had no money.
   = I would have gone, but I had no money.

3 ． a ． happen 爲不及物動詞，故不可用被動語態。
　　 b ． (C)爲過去未來式，可是事情現在已發生，故時態不對。
　　 c ． (D)本句爲疑問句，故不必用『did ＋ 原形動詞』來強調。

4 ． a ． (B)主要子句 I thought 爲過去式，故附屬子句不可能用
　　　　未來式。
　　 b ． already 應置於完成式助動詞 had 之後。
　　 c ． (A) rang 應改爲過去分詞 rung。

5 ． a ． (A)時態錯誤，因主要子句是過去式，故附屬子句不可能用未來
　　　　式。
　　 b ． (B) was coming ＝ would come
　　 c ． (C) coming 不可能用在完成進行式中。
　　　　He has come. (○)
　　　　（他已來了。）
　　　　He has been coming. (×)
　　　　（他一直都在來。）

6 ． must have ＋ P.P. 表示對過去事實之推測。

7 ． 主要子句爲未來式時，條件句一定是現在式。

8 ． before 子句的動作一定是最後發生，故用過去式。

9 ． as yet　　　仍然
　　 本片語常用於否定意味的完成式句子中。

1 0 ． before 引導的子句若爲過去式，爲了表示更早之前的行爲，主
　　　 要子句常用過去完成式。

1 1 ． 表未來某時正在進行的動作，用未來進行式。

1 2 ． 表示比過去式中的動作更早發生的事情，用過去完成式。

1 3 ． 表示從過去至今仍在持續的狀態或行爲，用現在完成進行式。

14. have done with　　辦完……
表時間的副詞子句必須用現在式代替未來式，本句中為了表示副詞子句中的行為先於主要子句，故用現在完成式。

15. hear (聽到)，see (看到)，smell (聞到)，feel (感覺到)
等動詞本身不用進行式。

16. while (當……時)，引導的副詞子句表示持續的狀態或行為，故常用進行式。

17. 表時間的副詞子句中，必須用現在式代替未來式。

18. 本句中的主要子句雖為未來式，但名詞子句中的事件為過去發生，故用過去式。
negotiation [nɪˌgoʃɪ'eʃən] n. 協商，談判
behind the scenes　　幕後，私底下
= behind the curtain

19. since 引導時間副詞子句時，該子句用過去式，主要子句用現在完成(進行)式。

20. 『by + 時間名詞』出現句中時，該句常用未來完成式或過去完成式。

21. (A) will 應改為 would。

22. (A) 應改為 may have migrated (當時很可能移至) 或 must have migrated (當時一定移至)，表對過去事實的推測。originaly 表示『原先』，是敘述過去概念，故不可用現在完成式。

23. (B) has become 應改為 became
敘述過去的事實用過去式。

24. (B) drank 應改為 drinking
He has been sitting...and drinking...

2 5. (B) live 應改為 lived
before he died 暗示 He has already died and is no longer
in the world. 故 who lives 應改為過去式 who lived。

2 6. (B) 應改為 to develop
不定詞之前若有完成式之動詞，不得再用完成式。

2 7. (C) 應改為 have never learned
過去完成式不得與現在式連用，要與過去式連用。
例: I think he had gone. (×)
I think he has gone. (○)
I wish he had gone.
(○，wish 之後的子句表與過去相反的假設語氣)

2 8. (B) 應改為 had been bitten
last time 引導的子句為過去式，故主要子句應為過去完成式。

2 9. (C) 應改為 considered
兩子句發生在過去的同時，故應用過去式。

3 0. (C) never knew 應改為 have never known
(B) 為現在完成式，故時間包括到現在，因此(C)不能用過去式。

第七章

假設語氣

概說:

　　假設語氣(subjunctive mood)是一種表示假設狀態的句型，由 if 引導的副詞子句與主要子句構成。依時態的不同而形成下列四種基本句型:

> a. 純條件的假設語氣
> b. 與現在事實相反的假設語氣
> c. 與過去事實相反的假設語氣
> d. 與未來狀況相反的假設語氣

茲列舉四種代表性的例句如下:

　a. 純條件的假設語氣——用現在式

　　If he is here, I will beat him.
　　(如果他在這兒，我會揍他。)

　b. 與現在事實相反的假設語氣——用過去式

　　If he were here, I would beat him.
　　(But he is not here.)
　　(如果他現在在這兒，我會揍他。——但他現在不在這兒。)

　c. 與過去事實相反的假設語氣——用過去完成式

　　If he had been here, I would have beaten him.
　　(But he was not here.)
　　(如果他當時在這兒，我會揍他。——但他當時不在這兒。)

d. 與未來狀況相反的假設語氣——if 子句要用助動詞 should,
主要子句則用過去式或現在式助動詞。

If he should be here, I would (或 will) beat him.
(萬一他在這兒,我會揍他。)

第一節 純條件假設語氣

1. 使用純條件假設語氣時,if 子句的動詞用現在式,主要子句
則用現在式助動詞。

句型如下:

	will may can should shall must ought to	
If + 主詞 + 現在式動詞,主詞 +		+ 原形動詞

例: If he is here, I will beat him.
(如果他在這兒,我會揍他。)

If anyone makes such a mistake, he must be
punished.
(誰要犯了這樣的錯誤,就要受處罰。)

If he comes, you should (ought to) tell him
the truth.
(如果他來了,你就該告訴他事情的真相。)

2. 使用純條件假設語氣時,要注意下列幾點:

a. 純條件假設語氣的 if 子句中,時態爲現在式,表示若 if

的條件存在，就會有預期的結果。在上列的第一個例句中 : If he is here, I will beat him. 即告訴我們，他要是在這兒，我就會揍他。至於他現在是否在這兒，我們不知道。我們只知，『他要是在這兒』這個條件存在的話，就會有『我就會揍他』的預期結果。

b. 表純條件句構的副詞連接詞不只 if 一種。Once(一旦)，when(當)，before(在……之前)，as soon as(一旦)等副詞連接詞亦可構成條件句，其用法與 if 相同。

例: Once I have money, I will buy a car.
　　　 現在式動詞　　　現在式助動詞
(一旦我有錢，我會買輛車。)

When he finishes it, he may come.
　　　　 現在式動詞　　現在式助動詞
(他做完事，就可以來了。)

c. 通常助動詞不置於 if 子句中，只置於主要子句中。

例: If the news is true, he may be safe.
　　　　　　　動詞　　　　　助動詞
(如果消息屬實，他很可能仍安然無恙。)

If the news will be true, he may be safe. (×)
　　　　　　助動詞　　　　　　助動詞

但: if 子句的主詞為人時，可用 can(能夠)或 will(願意)，must(非要……不可)等助動詞。

例: If he can come, I will be happy.
(如果他能來的話，我會很高興。)

If he will do it, I will be happy.
= If he is willing to do it, I will be happy.
(如果他願意做的話，我會很高興。)

If he <u>must</u> do it, he should do it with care.
= If he <u>has to</u> do it, he should do it with care.
（如果他非這樣做不可的話，他得小心做。）

注意：
If he will...的用法比較少見，最好避免。

d. 我們已知純條件假設語氣的主要子句中，助動詞均用現在
式，但 should 爲唯一例外。因爲 should 表示『應當』
之意，等於 ought to，故不受限制。

例：If I have time, I $\begin{vmatrix} \text{should} \\ \text{ought to} \end{vmatrix}$ do it.

（如果我有時間，我應當去辦這件事。）

但：If I <u>have</u> time, I <u>could</u> do it. (×)
　　　　↑　　　　　　↑
　　　　時態不一致

→ If I <u>have</u> time, I <u>can</u> do it. (○)
　　　　↑　　　　　　↑
　　　　時態一致
（如果我有時間，我可以做這件事。）

e. 原本純條件假設語氣的 if 子句中，動詞時態要用現在
式，但亦可用<u>原形動詞</u>，以凸顯條件的重要性。

例：If anyone <u>makes</u> the mistake, he should be punished.
　　　　　　　現在式
= If anyone <u>make</u> the mistake, he should be punished.
　　　　　　原形動詞
（如果有人犯錯就要被處罰。）

　　If he <u>is</u> mistaken, I will punish him.
= If he <u>be</u> mistaken, I will punish him.
（如果他搞錯的話，我會處罰他。）

注意:
此類原形動詞的用法比較少見，宜避免之。

第二節

與現在事實相反的假設語氣

1 . 使用本假設語氣時，if 子句的動詞用過去式，主要子句則用
過去式助動詞。句型如下：

| If ＋ 主詞 ＋ 過去式動詞，主詞 ＋ would / could / might / should / ought to ＋ 原形動詞 |

例：If I were rich, I would help you.
（如果我很有錢，我會幫助你。）

If he lived in my town, I could see him
every day.
（如果他住在我住的鎮上，我就能每天見到他。）

2 . 使用與現在事實相反的假設語氣時，要注意下列要點：

a . 本假設語氣旨在表示與現在事實相反的情況。換言之，一
見到此類過去式句型出現時，我們就可確知事實並非如此。

例：If I were rich, I would help you.
＝ As I am not rich, I can't help you.
（因為我不是很有錢，所以無法幫助你。）

They might finish the work before dark, if
we helped them.
＝ In fact, it is impossible that we will help

them, so they can't finish the work before dark.
(如果我們幫他們的話，天黑前他們就可以做完工作
了。——其實，我們不可能幫助他們，所以天黑前他
們也做不完工作。)

b. 不論主詞為第幾人稱，if 子句中的 be 動詞，均使用
were。

例: If you were in my shoes, what would you
do ? (○)
(如果你站在我的立場，你會怎麼做？)

If I was you, I wouldn't do it. (×)
→ If I were you, I wouldn't do it. (○)
(如果我是你，我不會做這事。)

c. 主要子句中的助動詞一定為過去式。如: will → would,
may → might, can → could, shall → should 或
ought to。但 must(必須) 只能表示現在或未來的狀況，
故只用於純條件的假設語氣，而絕不可用於表與現在事實
或過去事實相反的假設語氣中。

例: If you did it for me, I should be very
happy. (○)
(如果你為了我這樣做，我會很高興。)

If I could fly, I would fly to you.
(如果我能飛，我會飛向你。)

If you had money, you must help the poor. (×)
→ If you had money, you ought to help the poor. (○)
→ If you had money, you should help the poor. (○)
(如果你有錢，你應該幫助窮人。)
或 If you have money, you | must | help the poor. (○)
                          | should |
                          | ought to |

第三節

與過去事實相反的假設語氣

1. 本假設語氣中，if 子句的動詞要用過去完成式，主要子句則是助動詞的過去式，再加 『have ＋ 過去分詞』。
   句型如下：

If ＋ 主詞 ＋ had ＋ p.p., 主詞 ＋	would could might should ought to	＋ have ＋ p.p.

例：If I had arrived by three, I could have met him.
（要是我在三點前到，就能見到他了。）

If he had taken your advice, he might have been happier.
（要是他當時聽了你的勸告，他可能會快樂些。）

2. 使用與過去事實相反的假設語氣時，要注意下列要點：

a. 本假設語氣旨在表示與過去事實相反的情況。換言之，一見到此類過去完成式的句型出現時，我們就確知當時的事實並非如此。

If I had arrived by three, I could have met him.
（如果我三點前到，我就可以見到他。）
= As I didn't arrive by three, I didn't meet him.
（因為我沒有在三點前到，所以沒見到他。）

If he had taken your advice, he might have been happier.

（如果他當時接受你的建議，他可能會快樂些。）
= As he didn't take your advice, he wasn't happier.
（因他當時沒聽從你的勸告，所以他並沒有快樂點。）

If you had been in my shoes, you might have done it.
（如果當時你是站在我的立場，你可能會做這件事。）
= As you were not in my shoes, you didn't do it.
（因為當時你不是站在我的立場，所以你沒有做這件事。）

b. 注意 if 子句中 had 與 had had 的區別：
(1) if + 主詞 + had + 名詞時，had 為過去式動詞，譯成『有』，此為表示與現在事實相反的假設語氣。主要子句置過去式的助動詞即可。

例：If he had money, he might buy a car.
（如果他現在有錢，他可能會買輛汽車。）

(2) if + 主詞 + had + 過去分詞時，had 為過去完成式的助動詞，譯成『曾經』或『已經』，此時為表示與過去事實相反的假設語氣。主要子句用過去式的助動詞 + have + 過去分詞。

例：If he had had money, he might have bought a car.
（如果他當時有錢的話，他可能已經買輛車了。）

故：If he had money, he might have bought a car. (×)

第四節

與未來狀況相反的假設語氣

1. 使用本假設語氣時，if 子句一定要加助動詞 should。若假設的可能性很低，則主要子句要置過去式助動詞(和與現在事實相反的假設語氣相同)，但若假設的可能性很高，則主要子句要用現在式助動詞(與純條件假設語氣相同)。句型如下：

    a. 低可能性：

    If + 主詞 + should + 原形 V, 主詞 + 　would
    　　　　　　　　　　　　　　　　　　 could
    　　　　　　　　　　　　　　　　　　 might   + 原形 V
    　　　　　　　　　　　　　　　　　　 should
    　　　　　　　　　　　　　　　　　　 ought to

    例: If you should fall ill, the meeting would be put off.
    (萬一你生病，會議將延期。——你不太可能生病，會議不太可能延期。)

    If it should rain, I could stay home.
    (萬一下雨，我就能留在家裡。——不太可能下雨，而我也不太可能留在家裡。)

    b. 高可能性：

    If + 主詞 + should + 原形 V, 主詞 + 　will
    　　　　　　　　　　　　　　　　　　 can
    　　　　　　　　　　　　　　　　　　 may   + 原形 V
    　　　　　　　　　　　　　　　　　　 should
    　　　　　　　　　　　　　　　　　　 ought to

例: If you should fall ill, the meeting will be
put off.
(萬一你生病，會議將延期。——你可能會生病，而會
議亦可能延期。)

注意:
表與未來狀況相反的假設語氣，亦可與命令句形成的主要子
句並用。

例: If I should be late, be sure to wait for me.
(萬一我遲到，務必要等我。——我可能會遲到，你務必
要等我。)

第五節

使用假設語氣注意事項

1. 表強烈的與眞理相反的假設語氣，習慣用下列句型：

If ＋ 主詞 ＋ <u>were to</u> ＋ 原形 V, ＋ 主詞 ＋ | would
could
might
should
ought to | ＋ 原形 V

例：眞理：The cat can't smile.
　　　　　（貓不會笑。）
　　　假設：If the cat <u>were to</u> smile, I <u>would</u> pass out.
　　　　　（假如貓會笑，我會昏倒。）

　　　眞理：The sun doesn't rise in the west.
　　　　　（太陽不會打從西邊升起。）

　　　假設：If the sun <u>were to</u> rise in the west, how
　　　　　surprised the sunflower <u>would</u> be.
　　　　　（要是太陽打從西邊升起，向日葵會多麼吃驚啊！）

2. if 的省略
　　假設語氣的 if 子句中，若有過去完成式助動詞 had，或表
　　『萬一』的助動詞 should 或是 were 出現時，可將這些詞類
　　置於主詞前，而將 if 省略。

　　a. had

　　　例：If he <u>had</u> done it, he would have felt sorry.

= Had he done it, he would have felt sorry.
（如果他當時做了這件事，他會後悔的。）

b. should

例: If he should tell lies, I would punish him.
= Should he tell lies, I would punish him.
（要是他說謊，我會處罰他。）

c. were

例: If he were lazy, he might fail.
= Were he lazy, he might fail.
（如果他怠惰，他就可能會失敗。）

3. 時態不一致的假設
也就是 if 子句與過去事實相反，用過去完成式，主要子句
與現在事實相反則置過去式助動詞。句型如下：

If...had + p.p., 主詞 +	would could might should ought to	+ 原形 V +	now today

例: If I had been rich, I could buy a car now.
（如果我很有錢，我現在就能買輛車。）

If I had met her five years ago, she might be my
wife today.
（如果五年前我遇見了她，今天她可能就是我的妻子。）

If I had been rich, I could have bought a car
now. (×)

4. If he is nice... = If he be nice...
純條件假設語氣中的 if 子句動詞時態爲現在式，亦可改爲

原形動詞。

例: If he <u>takes</u> my place, I shall not have to go.
　= If he <u>take</u> my place, I shall not have to go.
　（如果他代替我，我應該就不必去了。）

　　If he <u>is</u> nice, I will make friends with him.
　= If he <u>be</u> nice, I will make friends with him.
　（如果他人很好，我會和他做朋友。）

但此類使用原形動詞的句構畢竟少見，故同學不宜使用，仍
以現在式的寫法為佳。

5. if = in case (that), on condition that, provided (that),
suppose (that), supposing (that), so long as （只要），
as long as （只要），此類連接詞通常只用在表純條件的假設語氣
中。換言之，其引導的子句時態均為現在式。

例: If it <u>is</u> fine, we will start to do it.
　（如果天氣好，我們就開始著手做這件事。）

　　<u>In case</u> he <u>comes</u>, let me know.
　= <u>In case</u> he <u>should</u> come, let me know.
　（如果他來了，讓我知道一下。）

　　I will undertake it <u>on condition that</u> you <u>bear</u>
　　the expenses.
　（如果是你出錢，這件事我就做。）

　　I will pardon him <u>provided (that)</u> he <u>acknowledges</u>
　　his mistake.
　（如果他認錯，我會原諒他。）

　　| Suppose
　　| Supposing ｜ I <u>meet</u> him, what shall I tell him?

（要是我遇見他，要跟他說什麼呢？）

Any book will do, as long as it is interesting.
（那本書都可以，只要有趣就好。）

注意:
in case + (that) 子句　　萬一……
in case of + 名詞　　　　萬一……

例: In case an accident happens, don't panic.
　= In case of an accident, don't panic.
（萬一有意外發生，不要驚慌。）

6. 若非／要不是……
此類句型僅限於與現在事實及過去事實相反的假設語氣

a. 與現在事實相反: 若非……就……

If it were not + But for + 名詞，	that 子句， （現在式） for + 名詞，	主詞 +	could would might should ought to	+ 原形 V

例: If it were not that he works hard, I wouldn't
like him.　　　　現在式動詞
　= If it were not for his hard work, I...
　　　　　　　　名詞
　= Were it not for his hard work, I...
　　　　　　　　名詞
　= But for his hard work, I...
　　　　　名詞
（要不是他很努力工作，我不會喜歡他。）

b. 與過去事實相反: 若非當時……就……

If it had not been │ that 子句 (過去式), │ +
　　　　　　　　　　│ for + 名詞, 　　　　│

主詞 + │ would 　│
　　　　│ could 　│
　　　　│ might 　│ + have + p.p.
　　　　│ should 　│
　　　　│ ought to │

例: If it had not been that he lent me the money,
　　　　　　　　　　　　　　　　　過去式動詞
　　I could not have bought that book.
= If it had not been for the money (which) he lent
　me, I...　　　　　　　　　　名詞
= Had it not been for the money (which) he lent me,
　I...　　　　　　　　　　　名詞
= But for the money (which) he lent me, I...
　　　　　　名詞
(要不是當時他借錢給我，我無法買到那本書。)

注意:
but for 亦可用介系詞 without 代替，之後仍接名詞。

例: But for his help, I couldn't do it.
= Without his help, I ....
(若非他的幫忙，我無法辦這事。)

　But for his timely warning, I might have been
　killed.
= Without his timely warning, I might have
　been killed.
(若非他及時警告，我可能已經被殺了。)

7. lest...should...　　　以免
　lest 為副詞連接詞，引導副詞子句。在該子句中，助動詞一

律用 should。 而 should 往往予以省略，故該子句中的一般
動詞必定是原形動詞。

例: I got up early lest I (should) miss the train.
(我早起以免錯過火車。)

I came on time lest he (should) be angry.
(我準時到，免得他生氣。)

注意:
lest...should...
= for fear that...|may　(表現在或未來的狀況)
　　　　　　　　　|might　(表過去的狀況)
= for fear of + 動名詞

例: You must study hard lest you should fail the exam.
= You must study hard for fear that you may fail the
exam.
= You must study hard for fear of failing the exam.
(你必須用功唸書，以免考試失敗。)

He did it carefully lest he should make a mistake
again.
= He did it carefully for fear that he might make a
mistake again.
= He did it carefully for fear of making a mistake
again.
(他很謹慎地做這件事，惟恐再次犯錯。)

8 . as if = as though 　　彷彿
as if 或 as though 均為副詞連接詞，引導副詞子句，使用
時有三種時態：
a . 表極大的可能→ 動詞使用一般時態

例: It looks as if (as though) it is going to rain.
(看起來好像要下雨了。)

b. 表與現在事實相反→ 動詞使用過去式

例: He loves me as though (as if) I were his own child.
（他愛我就像我是他的孩子一樣。）

c. 表與過去事實相反→ 動詞使用過去完成式

例: He looks as if (as though) nothing had happened.
（他看起來就像是什麼事都不曾發生過。）

注意:
as if 或 as though 之後亦可接不定詞片語，表示即將發生的狀況。

例: She opened her lips as if (she were going) to speak.
（她張開雙唇好像有話要說。）

9. what if...should...?　　要是……該怎麼辦？
本句型乃表示與未來狀況相反的假設語氣。if 子句恆置助動詞 should。

例: What if he should come ?
= What | might happen | if he should come ?
　　　 | could I (we) do |
（要是他來了，怎麼辦？）

What if it should rain?
= What | might happen | if it should rain?
　　　 | could I (we) do |
（要是下雨了，怎麼辦？）

10. It is
$\begin{vmatrix} \text{time} \\ \text{about time} \\ \text{high time} \end{vmatrix}$ + that 子句的過去式

該是……的時候了

注意:
使用本句型時，that 子句的動詞要用過去式。

例: It is time (that) he <u>went</u> to bed.
(該是他上床睡覺的時間了。)

本句暗示，現在該是他睡覺的時候了，但他沒有睡覺。其動作與現在事實相反，故用過去式。

例: It is time we <u>were</u> off.
(是我們該走的時候了。)

It is high time our children <u>had</u> some learning.
(是我們的孩子該學點東西的時候了。)

注意:
上列句構亦可改爲不定詞型態:

例: It is time he went to bed.
= It is time <u>for him</u> <u>to go</u> to bed.

It is high time our children had some learning.
= It is high time <u>for our children</u> <u>to have some</u>
<u>learning.</u>

11. If only... 要是……就好了
本句型只用於與現在事實或過去事實相反的假設語氣中。換言之，本句型的時態只能用過去式或過去完成式。

例: If only he <u>were</u> here.

= If he <u>were</u> here, it <u>would</u> be better.
(要是他現在在這裡就好了。)

  If only I <u>had known</u> it earlier.
= If I <u>had known</u> it earlier, it <u>would have been</u>
  better.
(要是我早點知道這件事就好了。)

１２. wish 的用法

a. wish 之後接 that 子句時，一定要使用假設語氣。
若與現在事實相反，要用過去式；若與過去事實相反，則要
用過去完成式。換言之 that 子句中的時態絕無現在式。

例: I wish (that) he <u>is</u> here. (×)
   I wish he <u>were</u> here. (○)
 = It is a pity that he <u>is</u> not here.
  (我真希望他現在就在這裡。但遺憾的是，他並不在這
  裡。)

   I wish he <u>had been</u> here. (○)
 = It is a pity that he <u>was</u> not here.
  (我真希望他當時就在這裡。但遺憾的是，他並不在這
  裡。)

b. I wish (that)...　　希望……
 = I would rather (that)...
 = Would that...

例: I wish (that) I had learned English harder.
 = <u>I would rather</u> (that) I had learned English
  harder.
 = <u>Would</u> that I had learned English harder.
  (真希望我當時能更用心地學英文。)

注意:

(1) would rather 之後本有動詞 wish,但在本句構中予以省略。

例: I <u>would rather wish</u> he were here.
= I <u>would rather</u> he were here.
(眞希望他現在就在這裡。)

(2) 使用 would that 句構時,亦可被 0 that 代替。但 that 通常不予省略,且句尾置驚嘆號 " ! "。

例: <u>Would that</u> I had done it.
<u>0 that</u> I had done it!
唯此類句構較爲罕見,同學應避免使用。

13. hope 的用法
hope 之後接 that 子句時,使用一般時態。即表現在的狀況時用現在式,表未來的狀況時用未來式,表完成的狀況時用完成式,表進行的狀況時用進行式。

例: a. 表現在狀況:
I <u>hope</u> (that) he <u>is</u> safe.
(我希望他安然無恙。)

b. 表未來狀況:
I <u>hope</u> he <u>will be</u> back.
(我希望他會回來。)

c. 表進行狀況:
I <u>hope</u> they <u>are having</u> a good time.
(我希望他們玩得愉快。)

d. 表完成狀況:
I <u>hope</u> they <u>have finished</u> the work.
(我希望他們已經把工作做好了。)

14. I hope 與祈使句的關係

I hope 接 that 子句時，子句中可使用助動詞 may，形成祈使句。此時將 I hope that 刪除，將 may 置於原 that 子句的主詞之前，動詞仍用原形動詞。原句點改爲驚嘆號。

例： I hope (that) he may live long.
　= May he live long!
　（願他長命百歲！）

　　 I hope you may pass the exam.
　= May you pass the exam!
　（祝你通過考試！）

注意：
a. 以 God 爲主詞時，可省略 may。

　例： I hope God may bless you.
　　= May God bless you!
　　= God bless you!
　　（上帝保佑你！）

b. 表『國家萬歲』時，亦可採倒裝句構。

　例： I hope the Republic of China may live long.
　　= May the Republic of China live long!
　　= Long live the Republic of China!
　　（中華民國萬歲！）

15. wish 和 hope 的異同

a. 相同部份：
(1) 均可用不定詞做受詞

　例： I wish to travel abroad.
　　= I hope to travel abroad.
　　（我希望能出國旅遊。）

(2) 亦可做不及物動詞,與介系詞 for 並用,表『期望獲得』之意,以名詞做其受詞。

例: I wish for a chance to try it.
   = I hope for a chance to try it.
   (我希望能有機會嘗試一下。)

I │ wish │ a chance to try it. (×)
  │ hope │

b. 不同部份:

(1) 表『祝福』時,只能使用 wish,之後接兩個名詞或代名詞做其受詞。

例: I wish you a good time.
   (祝你們玩得愉快。)

   I wish John success in the examination.
   (我希望約翰考試順利。)

   I hope you a good time. (×)
但: I hope (that) you may have a good time. (○)
   (我希望你們能玩得愉快。)

   I hope John success in the exam. (×)
但: I hope (that) John may be successful in the exam. (○)
   (我希望約翰能順利通過考試。)

(2) wish 可做不完全及物動詞,加了受詞之後,可用不定詞片語做受詞補語。hope 則無此用法。

例: I wish him to do it. (○)
         受詞 不定詞片語
   (我希望他做這件事。)

I hope him to do it. (×)

16. 對過去事物的猜測有三種句型:

a. must have + 過去分詞　　一定曾經……
   例: He is learned; he must have received higher education.
   (他博學多聞,一定受過較高的教育。)

b. may have + 過去分詞　　可能曾經……

   例: He looks tired; he may have stayed up late last night.
   (他看起來很疲倦,可能昨晚熬夜到很晚。)

c. cannot have + 過去分詞　　不可能曾經……

   例: He is honest; he cannot have stolen Mary's money.
   (他是老實人,不可能偷瑪麗的錢。)

注意:
若表猜測的句構爲疑問句時,要用『can...have...?』句型。

例: Can he have done it? (○)
   (他可能做了這樣的事嗎?)

   May he have done it? (×)

17. didn't need to.../need not have + p.p. 的比較
   didn't need to...乃表過去的事實,即『不必……同時亦没有如此做。』而 need not have + p.p. 乃與過去事實相反的假設語氣,即『不必……但卻這麼做了。』

   例: As I had enough money, I didn't need to borrow any from him.
   (由於錢夠,我當時不必向他借錢。——而且我也没借。)

Since you had enough money, you <u>needn't have</u>
<u>borrowed</u> money from me, but why did you still
borrow some?
(既然你的錢夠用，你就不必向我借了，為什麼你還要
借錢呢？)

18. 意志動詞計有『建議』，『要求』，『命令』，『規定』等四
大類。之後用 that 子句做受詞時，that 子句中要使用助
動詞 should。而 should 往往予以省略。

　　a. 建議: suggest, recommend, advise, urge(呼籲),
　　　　　　 propose, move(提議)

　　b. 要求: ask, desire, demand, require, request,
　　　　　　 insist(堅持要求)

　　c. 命令: order, command

　　d. 規定: rule, regulate, stipulate, maintain
　　　例: They <u>suggested</u> that he (<u>should</u>) <u>come</u> home on
　　　　　time.
　　　　　(他們建議他準時回家。)

　　　　　Mary <u>desired</u> that Peter (<u>should</u>) <u>treat</u> her
　　　　　nicely.
　　　　　(瑪麗請求彼得好好待她。)

　　　　　The umpire <u>ordered</u> that the player (<u>should</u>) <u>be</u>
　　　　　ousted.
　　　　　(裁判命令該選手出場。)

　　　　　The principal <u>ruled</u> that no student (<u>should</u>)
　　　　　play truant.
　　　　　(校長規定學生不准逃學。)

19. insist 若表『堅信』，maintain 若表『堅決認為』，

suggest 若表『暗示』，則之後的 that 子句用一般時態。

例: His words | suggested | that he wasn't telling a lie.
　　　　　　| implied　 |
　　　　　　| hinted 　 |
（他的話中暗示他絕不是在說謊。）

　　John | maintained | that he had met the girl before.
　　　　 | believed　 |
（約翰確信他曾經見過那女孩。）

　　He | insists　　　 | that the job isn't so difficult
　　　 | is convinced |
　　　 | is sure　　　 |
　　as one may think.
（他深信這份工作沒有一般人所想的那麼困難。）

20. | insist　on | + 動名詞　　堅決要求……
　　 | persist in |

例: He | insisted on　 | doing it that way.
　　　 | persisted in |
（他堅持要那樣做。）

21. 表『有必要的』形容詞，修飾 that 子句時，該子句亦須使用助動詞 should，而 should 往往予以省略。

注意:
此類形容詞通常有八個，均譯成『有必要的』:
necessary, important, essential, imperative, urgent,
desirable, recommendable, advisable

例: It is necessary that he (should) work hard.
（他必須努力工作。）

　　I think it essential that he (should) finish it

before leaving.
(我認為他必須在離開前做完這件事。)

It is desirable that he (should) not be lazy again.
(他一定不能再怠惰了。)

22. that 子句若是置於意志動詞變成的名詞之後，而與該名詞形
成同位語時，that 子句中也要使用助動詞 should，而
should 往往予以省略。

例: It is my suggestion that he (should) study abroad.
(我建議他出國唸書。)

They raised a proposal that the meeting (should)
be postponed.
(他們提議延期開會。)

It is John's desire that someone (should) help him
write the letter.
(約翰要求別人幫他寫信。)

Exercise

I. 請選出一個正確的答案:

1. What would you do if you _____ a million dollars?
   (A) have   (B) have had   (C) had   (D) shall have

2. Even if I _____, I wouldn't.
   (A) can   (B) shall   (C) could   (D) will

3. If he were living, he _____ twenty years old now.
   (A) will be   (B) would be
   (C) would have been   (D) is

4. I don't think you _____ me, even if I told you the truth.
   (A) will believe   (B) would have believed
   (C) would believe   (D) believed

5. If I had not called for a doctor, your friend _____.
   (A) had died   (B) will have died
   (C) will die   (D) would have died

6. I should have married her if she _____ such an extravagant girl.
   (A) were not   (B) wouldn't be
   (C) would not have been (D) hadn't been

7. If it _____ convenient, let's meet at nine o'clock.
   (A) is   (B) being   (C) was   (D) were

8. If he _____ in a day or two, I would wait for him.
   (A) will return   (B) returns
   (C) were to return   (D) had returned

9. If he _____ late, give him the message.
   (A) were coming   (B) would come
   (C) should come   (D) were come

10. _____ the doctor come a little sooner, the patient would have been saved.
    (A) Had   (B) Should   (C) Were   (D) If

11. _____ his aid, I could not have succeeded.
    (A) But   (B) Without   (C) Not   (D) Unless

12. I _____ abroad last year but for my illness.
    (A) would go   (B) would have gone
    (C) had gone   (D) went

13. I _____ but that he grasped me.
    (A) should have fallen   (B) should fall
    (C) had fallen   (D) fell

14. I wish I _____ as tall as she.
    (A) is   (B) was   (C) were   (D) be

15. Oh, if only I _____ your advice then.
    (A) take   (B) took   (C) should take   (D)had taken

16. She talks and acts as if she _____ abroad for a long time.
    (A) would have lived   (B) might live
    (C) lived   (D) had lived

17. Mr. Smith is, _____, a walking dictionary.
    (A) as it is   (B) as though

(C) as it were   (D) as if

18. He would rather people _____ about his family.
    (A) not talked   (B) hadn't talked
    (C) didn't talk   (D) wouldn't have talked

19. What if I _____ ?
    (A) failed   (B) should fail
    (C) would fail   (D) had failed

20. If he _____ in Germany, what language would he probably speak now?
    (A) were born   (B) have been born
    (C) had been born   (D) would have been born

II. 請選出錯誤的畫線部份：

21. They are the <u>ones</u> who <u>assert</u> that a better bridge
                    A   B
    <u>could</u> have been built <u>have</u> we had their assistance.
      C   D

22. <u>Had</u> anyone asked <u>him</u>, Barlow <u>could</u> <u>told</u> the investiga-
      A   B   C   D
    tors some useful details about the robbery.

23. If the cook had been more <u>careful</u> in <u>measuring</u> the
                                  A   B
    ingredients, the dinner <u>will</u> have been <u>much</u> better.
                              C   D

24. If you <u>would have</u> listened, you <u>too</u> would have concluded
              A   B
    that Peter is <u>more capable</u> than <u>any</u> other boy in his
                     C   D
    class.

25. Helen <u>will graduate</u> with her class <u>if</u> she had been
    　　　　　 A 　　　　　　　　　　　 B

    able <u>to meet</u> all of the requirements <u>in time</u>.
    　　　 C 　　　　　　　　　　　　　　　　 D

26. <u>Had</u> they had enough cash <u>on</u> hand, they <u>would buy</u> this
    　 A 　　　　　　　　　　 B 　　　　　 C

    fancy <u>furniture</u>.
    　　　　 D

27. If the volume of British investment is <u>to be</u> increased,
    　　　　　　　　　　　　　　　　　　　　　 A

    <u>other</u> demands on national resources <u>would have to</u> be
    　 B 　　　　　　　　　　　　　　　 C

    reduced or <u>eliminated</u>.
    　　　　　　 D

28. Sometimes I <u>get</u> the idea that a student is <u>expected</u> to
    　　　　　　 A 　　　　　　　　　　　　　 B

    think about getting educated for the sake of society as

    if he <u>was</u> not a part of <u>it</u>.
    　　　 C 　　　　　　 D

29. I sometimes wish that my university <u>is</u> <u>as large as</u> the
    　　　　　　　　　　　　　　　　　 A 　 B

    State University because our facilities are <u>more</u> limit-
    　　　　　　　　　　　　　　　　　　　　　 C

    ed <u>than</u> theirs.
    　 D

30. You <u>have confessed</u> that you <u>are</u> sorry for your rebel-
    　　 A 　　　　　　　　 B

    lion. So I <u>will</u> recommend that you <u>will not be punished</u>.
    　　　　　 C 　　　　　　　　　 D

標準答案：1.(C)　2.(C)　3.(B)　4.(C)　5.(D)　6.(D)　7.(A)
　　　　　8.(C)　9.(C)　10.(A)　11.(B)　12.(B)　13.(A)　14.(C)
　　　　　15.(D)　16.(D)　17.(C)　18.(C)　19.(B)　20.(C)　21.(D)
　　　　　22.(C)　23.(C)　24.(A)　25.(A)　26.(C)　27.(C)　28.(C)
　　　　　29.(A)　30.(D)

習題解答：

1．與現在事實相反的假設語氣

2．同上
　　even if　　即使

3．同上

4．同上

5．與過去事實相反的假設語氣

6．同上

7．此爲純條件句，並不表示與事實相反，故用現在式。

8．if + 主詞 + were to V, 主詞 + 過去式助動詞 + V
　　本句構表示未來不太可能發生的假設。

9．should 用於假設語氣的 if 子句中表『萬一』：
　　if + 主詞 + should V,｜主詞 +｜過去式助動詞｜V
　　　　　　　　　　　　｜　　　｜現在式助動詞｜
　　　　　　　　　　　　｜祈使句｜

10．if 子句中若有 had，可移至句首代替 if。

11．｜without｜N + 假設語氣子句　　　若非……
　　｜but for｜
　　本句表與過去事實相反。

１２. 同上

１３. but that｜現在式子句｜+ 假設語氣子句　　若非，要不是
　　　　　　　 ｜過去式子句｜
　　　本句中的主要子句表與過去事實相反。

１４. I wish + 假設語氣子句　　　但願
　　　本句表與現在事實相反。

１５. if only 用法有二:
　　　(1)假設法: 表『但願』。
　　　例:｜If only｜I were you.
　　　　　｜I wish ｜
　　　　　(我要是你就好了。)
　　　(2)條件句: 表『只要』。
　　　例:｜If only　　｜I have money, I'll buy a car.
　　　　　｜As long as｜
　　　　　(只要我有錢，我就要買車。)

１６. as if +｜過去式(與現在相反)　　　彷彿……
　　　　　　 ｜過去完成式(與過去相反)

１７. as it were　　　可以說是
　　＝ so to speak

１８.｜would rather｜+ that + 過去式子句　　　寧願……
　　 ｜had sooner ｜

１９. what if + 主詞 + should + V　　　萬一……怎麼辦

２０. 本句的前半部表示與過去事實相反，後半部表示與現在事實
　　　相反。

２１. 本句乃與過去事實相反的假設，故 have 應改為 had。
　　　had we had their assistance.
　　＝ ...if we had had their assistance.

22. could 要改為 could have，表與過去事實相反。

23. will 應改為 would。

24. would have 應改為 had，因為與過去相反的 if 子句中，要用過去完成式，不可與過去式助動詞並用。

25. if 子句中表與過去相反，故主要子句中的 will graduate 應改為 would have graduated。

26. would buy 應改為 would have bought。

27. 本句為純條件句，並非與事實相反的假設，故主要子句中的 would have to 應改為 will have to。
    注意:
    If...is to be increased
    = If...has to be increased

28. was 應改為 were。

29. is 應改為 were。

30. recommend 為意志動詞，其後的 that 子句中須用 should + V，而 should 通常省略，故 will not be punished 應改為 (should) not be punished。

第八章　副詞

概說:

英語中的副詞多半爲形容詞之後加 -ly 變化而成。
如:

形容詞:	副詞:
slow (慢的)	——→ slowly (慢地)
quick (快的)	——→ quickly (快地)
easy (容易的)	——→ easily (容易地)
main (主要的)	——→ mainly (主要地)

但亦有些副詞卻自成一格。
如:

very (非常地)	ago (以前)
hard (努力地)	enough (充分地)
never (從不)	somewhat (有點兒)
somehow (不知怎地)	

有的甚至用現在分詞做副詞用,專門修飾形容詞。

例: It's <u>biting</u> <u>cold</u> today.
　　　　 adv.　　 adj.

(今天天氣冷死了——冷得會咬人一樣。)
= It's <u>freezing</u> <u>cold</u> today.
　　　　　adv.　　　 adj.

(今天天氣冷死了——冷得要把人凍僵一樣。)

It's <u>boiling</u> <u>hot</u> today.
　　　 adv.　 adj.

（今天天氣熱死了——熱得要把水都煮沸了。）

妙的是，有些形容詞本身亦可當副詞用。

例：awful：His writing is <u>awful</u>.
                           adj.
      （他的文章糟透了。）

        He is | <u>awful</u> | <u>mad</u>.
               | adv. | adj.
               | very |
               | awfully |
      （他氣壞了。）

    fine：The dress is <u>fine</u>.
                         adj.
      （這套洋裝挺不錯的。）

        The dress <u>suits</u> me <u>fine</u>.
                     vt.   adv.
      （這套洋裝挺適合我的。）

更絕的是，good 與 and 合在一起，竟然也成了副詞，譯成
『非常』（= very）（只置於 be 動詞之後，修飾形容詞）。

例：It's <u>good and</u> <u>hot</u> today.
           adv.   adj.

    （今天熱死了。）

同學看到這裡，不禁會叫道：『慘了，副詞有那麼多奇怪的
形態，叫我不知如何是好？』雄哥認為，你無須害怕，也不
必一一死記所有的副詞形態及其用法。只要你多看文章，多
查字典，每天讀上三、四個小時英文(我有十年的時間幾乎每
天花十六個小時唸英文)，自然就會熟悉副詞的形態及其用法。

第一節
副詞的功能

1. 修飾動詞(包括動詞轉化的不定詞，動名詞，分詞)
此時副詞通常置於動詞之後：

例: He studies hard. (動詞)
   vt. adv.

(他很用功。)

  I love you very much. (動詞)
    vt.   adv.

(我非常愛妳。)

  You will have to study diligently. (不定詞)
          adv.
(你將必須努力用功。)

  Rising early is good for your health. (動名詞)
     adv.

(早起有益你的健康。)

比較: He speaks English good. (×)
    vt.   adj.

  He speaks English well. (○)
    vt.   adv.

(他英語說得好。)

2．修飾形容詞
　　此時副詞通常置於該形容詞之前：

　　　例：He is very kind.
　　　　　　　 adv.　adj.

　　　　（他人很好。）

　　　　It is extremely dangerous to swim alone.
　　　　　　　　　adv.　　　 adj.

　　　　（單獨游泳非常危險。）

　　比較：This is probable true. (×)
　　　　　　　　　 adj.　　adj.

　　　　This is probably true. (○)
　　　　　　　　 adv.　　adj.

　　　　（這很可能是眞的。）

3．修飾副詞
　　此時副詞通常置於該副詞之前：

　　　例：He studies very diligently.
　　　　　　　　　　 adv.　 adv.

　　　　（他非常努力用功。）

　　　　He does things too carefully.
　　　　　　　　　　 adv.　 adv.

　　　　（他做事過於謹愼。）

4．修飾全句
　　此時副詞通常置於句首：

例: <u>Fortunately</u> <u>he did not die.</u>
　　 adv. 　　　　全　句

（幸運地他沒死。）

<u>Evidently</u> <u>this answer is right.</u>
　　 adv. 　　　　全　句

（這答案顯然是對的。）

注意:
修飾全句的副詞一定是置於句首，若置於句尾，則會修飾句
中的動詞，而造成語意的偏差。

例: <u>Happily</u> <u>he did not die.</u>
　　 adv. 　　　　全　句

（所幸他沒死。）

<u>He did not die</u> <u>happily.</u>
　　　　　　 vi. 　 adv.

（他沒有快樂地過世。——他死時不快樂。）

第二節

副詞的位置

1 . 在含有 be 動詞（如 is, are, am, were, was），助動詞（如 can, shall, may, should, ought to, must）以及完成式助動詞（have, has, had），及動詞的句構中，一般副詞的位置有下列慣例：

a. 遇有 be 動詞時，副詞置於該 be 動詞之後。

例： He is always kind.（他爲人一直都很好。）

They are really able to do it.
（他們確實有能力做這件事。）

b. 遇有助動詞時，副詞置於該助動詞之後。

例： He can hardly walk.（他幾乎走不動了。）

He has never been to the United States before.
（他以前從未去過美國。）

c. 遇有動詞時，副詞置於該動詞之前。

例： They often go fishing.
　　　　adv. vi.

（他們常去釣魚。）

He really cares about you.
　　adv. vi.

（他眞的很在乎你。）

同學看到這裡，一定會問道：『在本章第一節中，雄哥曾說修飾動詞時，副詞應置於動詞之後，爲何此時又說副詞應置於動詞之前？』答案很簡單：

(1) 如果修飾動詞的副詞表示某種狀態，則副詞要置於動詞之後。

　　例：She dances beautifully. (○)
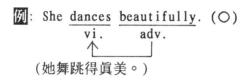

　　（她舞跳得眞美。）

　　　beautifully 乃表示跳舞的樣子很美(表示狀態)，故 beautifully 應置於 dances 之後。

　　同理：He 　drove 　(his car) fast.
　　　　　　vi. & vt. 　　　　　adv.

　　（他車開得很快。）

　　　fast 乃表示開車的速度很快，故 fast 應置於 drove (his car) 之後。

(2) 如果修飾動詞的副詞表示肯定、否定或頻率的意味，則此類副詞多置於動詞之前。

　　有肯定意味的副詞：surely（確定地），certainly（確定地），absolutely（絕對地），probably（可能）really（眞正地）。

　　有否定意味的副詞或頻率副詞：never（從不），seldom（很少），hardly ever（幾乎不會），always（總是），often（常常）。

例: I surely like him.
　　　 adv.　 vt.

(我當然喜歡他。)

They certainly hope to win the game.
　　　 adv.　 vt.

(他們當然希望贏得比賽。)

They always cheat.
　　　 adv.　　 vi.

(他們總是騙人。)

同學看到上面的解釋大概仍然不能完全了解雄哥想要表達的意思。沒關係，雄哥換下列方式來講解。

我們可用中英文句型做比較:

中文: 他跑得快。

英文: He ran fast. (○, fast 為狀態副詞)
　　　 vi. adv.

He fast ran. (×)

中文: 他真的愛你。

英文: He really loves you.
　　　 adv.　 vt.

(○, really 為肯定意味的副詞)
He loves you really. (×)

中文: 他常常上學遲到。

英文：He <u>often</u> <u>comes</u> to school <u>late</u>.
          adv.   vi.   adv.

（〇，often 爲頻率副詞，late 則爲狀態副詞）

由此可知，中英文有很多句構是互通的。但這種藉中英文比較來了解英語中副詞的位置，並不一定很準，同學唯有經由博覽文章才能學得習慣的用法，切記，切記！

2．在簡化句構中，表示肯定意味的副詞及頻率副詞之位置有下列變化：

   a．be 動詞

      簡化前：He <u>is really</u> nice.
             （他人眞好。）
      簡化後：He <u>really is</u>. （〇）
             He is really. （×）

      簡化前：They <u>are always</u> eager to learn English.
             （他們總是迫切想學英文。）
      簡化後：They <u>always are</u>. （〇）
             They are always. （×）

   b．助動詞

      簡化前：He <u>can hardly</u> do it.
             （他幾乎做不了此事。）
      簡化後：He <u>hardly can</u>. （〇）
             He can hardly. （×）

      簡化前：He <u>has never</u> done it before.
             （他從未做過此事。）
      簡化後：He <u>never has</u>. （〇）
             He has never. （×）

3．表狀態的副詞在被動語態中，要置於過去分詞前。

主動語態：He did the job well.
　　　　　　　vt.　　　　adv.

（他把工作做得很好。）

被動語態：The job was well done. （○）
　　　　　　　　　　　　adv.　p.p.

　　　　　The job was done well. （劣）

主動語態：They decorated the room beautifully.
　　　　　　　vt.　　　　　　　adv.

（他們把房間裝飾得很美。）

被動語態：The room was beautifully decorated. （○）
　　　　　　　　　　　　adv.　　　　p.p.

　　　　　The room was decorated beautifully. （劣）

4．否定副詞 never(從不)，seldom(很少)，hardly ever(幾乎不曾 = scarcely ever)，rarely(很少) 修飾動詞時，可直接置於該動詞之前，無須另加助動詞 do, does 或 did。但 not 不可直接置於動詞之前，須另加 do, does 或 did，且之後的動詞一律改為原形。

例：He never cheats. （○）
　　（他從不騙人。）

　　They seldom do what the teacher has taught them
　　　　　　　　vt.
　　to (do).
　　（他們很少去做老師要他們做的事。）

　　He hardly ever remained quiet.
　　　　　　　　　　　vi.

（他很少保持安靜。）

但: He <u>not cheats</u>. （×）
　　　　　　 vi.
→ He <u>does not cheat</u>. （○）
　　　　 原形 vi.
（他不騙人。）

They <u>not enjoy</u> singing. （×）
　　　　　 vt.
→ They <u>do not enjoy</u> singing. （○）
　　　　　 原形 vt.
（他們不喜歡唱歌。）

5．can 與 not 並用時，習慣上應寫成 cannot，而不使用 can not。

例: He <u>cannot</u> meet the requirement. （○）
（他達不到要求。）

He <u>can not</u> meet the requirement. （劣）

6．時間副詞，如 yesterday, today, tomorrow, this year, at five(五點鐘), in 1970，可置於句首或句尾。習慣的用法爲：句子短時，時間副詞置於句尾，句子長時，則置於句首。

長句: <u>Yesterday</u> I <u>saw</u> him chatting very pleasantly
with a blonde girl near the park.
（昨天我在公園附近看到他和一位金髮女郎聊得很開心。）

短句: I <u>saw</u> him in the park <u>yesterday</u>.

長句: <u>In 1914</u>, the battle <u>broke out</u> in the small town

close to the border.
（一九一四年，戰爭在邊境的小城中爆發。）

短句：The battle <u>broke out</u> <u>in 1914</u>.

7 . 地方副詞，如 here, there, home, downtown(城裡)，
upstairs(樓上)，downstairs(樓下)，以及表場所的介系詞，
如 on, out, up, down 等，均置於動詞之後。

例：He came │ here.
　　　　　　│ home.
　　　　　　│ in.
　　　　　　│ up.
（他　來這裡／回家／進來／上來。）

注意：
介副詞與介系詞的分別如下：

a. in, out, up, down 之後有受詞時，就稱為介系詞。

例：He sat <u>in</u> the <u>corner</u>.
　　　　　　介　　　o.
（他坐在角落裡。）

He looked <u>out</u> (of) <u>the window</u>.
　　　　　　　介　　　　　　o.
（他望向窗外。）

b. in, out, up, down 之後若無受詞，則為介系詞變成的副
詞，簡稱介副詞，視為地方副詞。

例：He came <u>in</u>. （他進來。）
　　　　　　介副詞

He rushed <u>out</u> crying.
　　　　　　介副詞

（他哭著衝了出去。）

He stepped down after the power struggle.
　　　　　介副詞
（他在權力鬥爭之後下台。）

8. 副詞對等語及其在句中的位置
副詞對等語即指由兩個以上的單字構成的片語或子句，具有副詞的功能，用以修飾句中的動詞或整個主要子句。

a. 副詞片語：
句括介系詞片語及不定詞片語兩類。

(1) 介系詞片語當副詞用：
通常置於句尾，修飾句中的動詞。

例: He loves her with all his heart.
　　　vt.　　　　介詞片語
↑

（他全心地愛她。）

He achieved the goal by working hard.
　　vt.　　　　　　介詞片語
↑

（他努力工作達成目標。）

He came by bus.
　　vi. 介詞片語
↑

（他坐公車來的。）

注意:
有時介系詞片語亦出現在句首，此時該片語仍被視為副詞，修飾整個主要子句。但亦有形容詞的功能，修飾主詞。此類介系詞片語多半由 in, by 或 on 加動名詞形成。

例: In doing the work, you must be careful.
　　　介詞片語　　　　　整要主要子句
　　　　　└──副詞──┘

= When you do the work, you must be careful.
　In doing the work, you must be careful.
　　　介詞片語　　　主詞
　　　　└─形容詞─┘

（做這工作時，你必須要謹慎。）

　By working hard, he achieved the goal.
　　介詞片語　　　整個主要子句
　　　└──── 副詞 ───┘

= Because he worked hard, he achieved the goal.
　By working hard, he achieved the goal.
　　介詞片語　　　主詞
　　　└── 形容詞──┘

（他努力工作達成目標。）

　|On　| seeing her, he ran away.
　|Upon|　　　　　　整個主要子句
　　　介詞片語
　　　　└── 副詞 ────┘

= As soon as he saw her, he ran away.

　|On　| seeing her, he ran away.
　|Upon|　　　　　　主詞
　　介詞片語
　　　└── 形容詞──┘

（一看到她，他就跑開了。）

注意:
in, by 或 on 加動名詞所形成的介系詞片語，置
於句首時，要合理的修飾主詞，也就是被修飾的主詞要
有行使動名詞所表現的能力。通常此類主詞一定是人。
否則易形成不連接修飾 (dangling modification)的錯

誤句構。

例：On seeing her, he ran away. (○)
　　　　　　　　　　人
理由：he 為人，故可以做出 seeing her 所表示
　　　的動作。

例：On seeing her, tears came into his
　　eyes. (×)　　　　　物

理由：tears 為眼淚，不能做出 seeing her 的
　　　動作。本句譯成：眼淚看見她之後，就湧入
　　　他的眼眶中。
　　　(不得了，他的眼淚會看見人，八成是個妖怪。)

例：In doing the work, he must be careful. (○)
　　　　　　　　　　　　人

理由：he 為人，故可做出 doing the work 所表
　　　示的動作。

例：In doing the work, care must be taken. (×)
　　　　　　　　　　抽象名詞

理由：care 為抽象名詞，表『謹慎』，顯然『謹
　　　慎』不能自己去做工作，故本句犯了不連接
　　　修飾的錯誤。

(2) 不定詞片語當副詞用：
　　不定詞片語當副詞用，除可修飾動詞外，亦可置於形容詞
　　或副詞之後，修飾該形容詞或副詞。

例：You will soon come to realize that you are
　　mistaken.　　　vi.

（你很快便會了解自己錯了。）

She <u>went to Italy</u> | in order | <u>to study music.</u>
　　　vi. | so as
　　　↑

（她去義大利學音樂。）

I am <u>sorry</u> <u>to have kept you waiting.</u>
　　　adj.

（我很抱歉讓你久等。）

He is <u>rich</u> <u>enough</u> <u>to buy a car</u>.
　　　adj.　adv.
　　　↑　　↑

（他有錢可以買部車。）

注意:

表目的的不定詞片語置於句首時，亦同時有副詞及形容詞的功能。做副詞用時，不定詞片語修飾整個主要子句；做形容詞用時，則修飾主要子句中的主詞，而該主詞亦要有行使不定詞片語中動詞所表現的動作能力，故該主詞亦通常為人，否則易造成不連接修飾的錯誤句構。

例: <u>To achieve the goal</u>, <u>you</u> must work hard.
　　　副詞片語　　　　　　主要子句
　　　　　　　　　　　　　　　↑

　　<u>To achieve the goal</u>, <u>you</u> must work hard.
　　　形容詞片語　　　　　人
　　　　　　　　　　　　↑

（要達成目標，你必須努力工作。）

　　To achieve the goal, <u>hard work</u> is necessary. （×）
　　　　　　　　　　　　抽象名詞

理由: hard work（努力）為抽象名詞，不可能自行 achieve

the goal，故形成不連接修飾。

但有些不定詞片語已成了固定的獨立副詞片語，稱爲獨立不定詞片語，置於句首時，只做副詞用，修飾整個主要子句。此時就不必顧慮主要子句的主詞。

例：<u>To do him justice</u>, <u>he is qualified for the</u>
　　　副詞片語　　　　　　主要子句

position.
（替他說句公道話，他有資格擔任此職位。）

<u>To be frank with you</u>, <u>the trip wasn't interesting</u>.
　　副詞片語　　　　　　　　主要子句

（老實跟你說，這次旅行並不好玩。）

<u>To sum up</u>, <u>one can't do without friends</u>.
　副詞片語　　　　整個子句

（總而言之，一個人不能沒有朋友。）

有關獨立不定詞的用法，我們已在本書上冊227頁敘述過，請同學自行參考。

b. 副詞子句：
在本書上冊第二章第三節，雄哥就已爲同學介紹了副詞子句的形成及其功能，在此不必贅述，然而值得重覆強調的就是：副詞子句多用來修飾整個主要子句，可置於主要子句前後。若置於主要子句之前時要加逗點。

例：<u>Because he is nice</u>, <u>I like him</u>.
　　副詞子句　　　　　主要子句
= <u>I like him</u> <u>because he is nice</u>.
　　主要子句　　　副詞子句
（我喜歡他因爲他很好。）

If you have time, will you do it?
<u>副詞子句</u>　　　<u>主要子句</u>(問句型)
= Will you do it if you have time?
　<u>主要子句</u>　　　<u>副詞子句</u>
(如果有空的話，你會不會做這件事？)

這種原則亦適用於副詞片語。
例: To achieve the goal, you must work hard.
　　<u>副詞片語</u>　　　　　<u>主要子句</u>
= You must work hard to achieve the goal.
　　　　　　　　　　　<u>副詞片語</u>
(要達成目標，你必須努力工作。)

By working hard, he achieved the goal.
<u>副詞片語</u>　　　　<u>主要子句</u>
= He achieved the goal by working hard.
　　　　　　　　　　<u>副詞片語</u>
(他努力工作達成了目標。)

9. 句中若含有兩組以上的動詞(包括由動詞變成的分詞及動名詞)，
副詞應盡量靠近被修飾的動詞，以免造成句意的混淆。

例: Yesterday he mentioned seeing her.
　　<u>adv.</u>　　　　<u>vt.</u>

(他昨天提到曾經見到她。)

He mentioned seeing her yesterday.
　　　　　<u>動名詞</u>　　　<u>adv.</u>

(他提到昨天曾經見到她。)

理由: yesterday 所放的位置不同，造成不同的句意。

例: You should <u>handle</u> the question <u>with care</u> that he
　　　　　　　vt.

raised yesterday.（劣）

（你應用那個昨天他提出來的謹慎來處理這個問題。）

理由：本來 with care（以謹慎的態度）是副詞，明確修飾動
　　　詞 handle。形容詞子句 that he raised yesterday
　　　本應修飾 the question 但卻因置於名詞 care 之後，
　　　造成句意的偏差。

改正：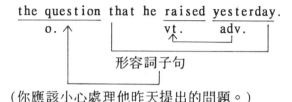

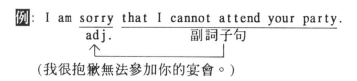

（你應該小心處理他昨天提出的問題。）

10. 名詞子句（由 that, whether 以及疑問詞 where, when, how
　　等構成）具有名詞的功能，在句中要做主詞，受詞，或 be
　　動詞之後的補語（見本書上冊19-26頁）。但名詞子句亦可置於
　　形容詞之後，此時即成副詞子句，修飾該形容詞。

　　例：I am sorry that I cannot attend your party.
　　　　　　　adj.　　　　　　副詞子句

　　（我很抱歉無法參加你的宴會。）

　　I am not sure whether he'll come.
　　　　　　adj.　　副詞子句

　　（我不確定他是否會來。）

第三節

重要的副詞用法

1. very, much

　a. very 不可修飾動詞，而 much（或 very much）則可。

　　例：I very like you. （×）
　　　　　　‾‾‾‾‾‾‾
　　　　　　　vt.

　　→ I like you (very) much. （○）
　　　　‾‾‾‾‾　　　　‾‾‾‾
　　　　vt.　　　　　adv.

　　　（我很喜歡你。）

　b. very 可修飾一般形容詞或副詞，但形容詞或副詞變成比較
　　　級時，則只能用 much 修飾。

　　例：He walked very slowly. （○）
　　　　　　　　　　‾‾‾‾
　　　　　　　　　　adv.

　　　（他走得很慢。）

　　　I'm very happy to be of service. （○）
　　　　　‾‾‾‾‾
　　　　　adj.

　　　（我很高興能幫得上忙。）

　　　He walked very more slowly than I. （×）

　　→ He walked much more slowly than I. （○）
　　　　　　　‾‾‾‾‾‾‾

　　　（他走得比我慢多了。）

He is very happier than Peter.（×）

→ He is much happier than Peter.（○）

（他比彼得快樂多了。）

c. 修飾 too 時只能用 much，不能用 very。

例：He is very too young.（×）

→ He is much too young.（○）

（他太年輕了。）

注意：
修飾比較級或 too 的副詞通常有六個：
much, far, a lot, a great deal, still, even

例：He is | much | more prudent than John.
| far | less diligent than John.
| a lot | better than John.
| a great deal | too old to do the work.
| still |
| even |

（他比約翰小多了。）
（他沒有約翰勤奮。）
（他比約翰好多了。）
（他太老了沒法做這事。）

d. 分詞做形容詞時：
very 修飾現在分詞，much 則修飾過去分詞。

例：She is indeed a very charming girl.

（她實在是個非常迷人的女孩。）

He raised a very interesting question.

(他提出一個非常有趣的問題。)

I was much annoyed with her son.

(我很氣惱她兒子。)

He was much interested in that book.

(他對那本書很有興趣。)

但: 有時 very 亦可用來修飾過去分詞。

例: He was very interested in that book.
　　　(= much)

同學翻遍各種文法參考書時,一定發現沒有任何一本會告訴你判斷的方法。別怕,雄哥有個方法,也就是用中英文的類比方式,保證萬無一失。
即: 先將英文中做形容詞用的過去分詞譯成中文,若可被中文的『很』修飾時,即可使用 very + 過去分詞。

例: He is very | tired. (很累的)
　　 = much | pleased. (很高興)
　　　　　　 | interested. (很感興趣)

否則只能用 much 修飾過去分詞。

例: He was very hurt. (很受傷) (×)
　→ He was much hurt. (他傷得很重。)

e. very 亦可當形容詞以修飾名詞,表『正是那個』,放在 the 之後。此時名詞之後若有形容詞子句修飾,其關係代名詞必為 that,取代 who, whom, which。

例: He is | the very man
       | just the man
       | the particular man
that came here yesterday.
(他就是昨天來的那位老兄。)

2. little, a little

a. little 做副詞時，譯成『幾乎一點兒都不』，等於 no
(一點兒都不) 之意。

例: The patient's condition is little better than
                                              adj.
(it was) yesterday.
= the patient's condition
(病人的情況並沒有比昨天好一點。)

b. a little 做副詞時，譯成『有點兒』。

例: The patient's condition is getting(= becoming)
a little better.
       adj.

(病人的情況好轉了些。)

c. little 做副詞時，通常修飾動詞 think, know, dream,
expect(期待)。

例: I little thought (或 dreamed, expected, knew)
that you had done it.
(我幾乎沒料到你已把事做完了。)

3. no longer   不再
= no more
= not...any longer

= not...any more

例: John is fired; he is <u>no longer</u> here.
　　　　　= he is <u>no more</u> here.
　　　　　= <u>no longer is</u> he here.
　　　　　= <u>no more is</u> he here.
　　　　　= he is <u>not</u> here <u>any longer</u>.
　　　　　= he is <u>not</u> here <u>any more</u>.
　(約翰被開除了; 他不再在這兒了。)

注意:
no longer 或 no more 由於是否定副詞, 故置於句首, 要採
倒裝句。

例: You can <u>no longer</u> see him.
→ <u>No longer can you</u> see him.
　(你再也見不到他了。)

　　He <u>no more</u> loves the girl.
→ <u>No more does he</u> love the girl.
　(他不再愛這女孩了。)

4. sometimes, sometime, some time, some times

a. sometimes　　有時候
此為頻率副詞(如 often, never, seldom 等), 使用時
通常置於句首, 亦可置於句尾。

例: <u>Sometimes</u> he comes here for a visit.
　= He comes here for a visit │ <u>every now and then</u>.
　　　　　　　　　　　　　　 │ <u>more often than not</u>.
　(他有時候來這兒拜訪一下。)

b. sometime　　某時(不知何時)
可用於過去式或未來式, 使用時通常與另一明確的時間

副詞或副詞片語並用。

例: 過去式:
　　I saw him <u>sometime</u> <u>yesterday morning</u>.
　　　　　　　　　　　　　　明確的時間副詞
　　(我昨天早上某個時間見過他。)

　　未來式:
　　I'll be here <u>sometime</u> <u>tomorrow</u>.
　　　　　　　　　　　　　　明確的時刻
　　(我明天某個時間會來這兒。)

c. some time 　　　一段時間

例: I'll stay here (for) <u>some time</u>.
　　(我會待在這兒一陣子。)

　　He was here <u>some time</u> ago.
　　(不久前他還在這兒。)

　　He was here sometime ago. (×)
理由: ago 非明確的時間副詞, 故無 sometime ago 的
　　　用法。

d. some times 　　　有幾次
 = a few times
 = several times

例: I have been to Thailand some times.
　　(我曾去過泰國幾次。)

5. ago, before, since, after

a. ago 表『距現在若干時間以前』, 時態用過去式。

例: He <u>came</u> here a few days ago.

（他幾天之前來過這兒。）

　How long ago <u>did</u> he come?
（他多久之前來的？）

比較：He <u>had finished</u> the work 2 hours ago. （×）
　　　　　過去完成式
　→ He <u>finished</u> the work 2 hours ago. （○）

b. before 表『距過去某時若干時間以前』，時態用過去完成式。

例：He told me that he <u>had seen</u> Mary a few days
　　　　　　　　　　　　　過去完成式
　　before.
（他告訴我幾天之前曾見過瑪莉。）

比較：He told me that he <u>had seen</u> Mary a few days
　　　<u>ago</u>. （×）
理由：ago 只能用在過去式的句構。

注意：ago 不能單獨使用，而 before 卻可以。即 before
　　　可單獨做副詞，修飾句中的動詞，通常與現在完成式
　　　，過去完成式，以及過去式並用。

例：I met him <u>ago</u>. （×）

I <u>met</u> him 2 hours <u>ago</u>. （○）
過去式

I <u>met</u> him <u>before</u>. （○）
過去式

I <u>have met</u> him <u>before</u>. （○）
現在完成式

I told him that I <u>had met</u> him <u>before</u>. (○)
　　　　　　　　　過去完成式

c. since 　　自從……

(1) 做副詞連接詞，引導過去式的副詞子句，修飾時態爲現在完成(進行)式或過去完成(進行)式之主要子句。

例：I have studied English <u>since</u> I <u>moved</u> here
　　 現在完成式　　　　　　　　　 過去式
　　 in 1971.
　　 (自從一九七一年搬來這裡後，我便一直唸英文。)

　　 He told me that he <u>had studied</u> English
　　　　　　　　　　　　　 過去完成式
　　 <u>since</u> he <u>moved</u> here in 1971.
　　　　　　　　 過去式
　　 (他告訴我自從一九七一年搬來這裡後，他便一直唸英文。)

(2) 做副詞用，修飾現在完成(進行)式，過去完成(進行)式之主要子句。since 譯成『之後』，可置於句尾，或句中 have, has, had 完成式助動詞之後。

例：I <u>moved</u> here in 1971 <u>and</u> <u>have studied</u>
　　 過去式　　　　　　　　　　　 現在完成式
　　 English <u>since</u>.
　 = I <u>moved</u> here in 1971 and <u>have</u> <u>since</u> studied
　　 English.
　　 (我於一九七一年遷到此處，之後就一直唸英文。)

注意：
since 做副詞時，句型結構一定爲：
主詞 +過去式動詞 + 明確時間副詞片語 + and + 主詞
+ have (has, had) + | since + 過去分詞 |
　　　　　　　　　　　　 | 過去分詞 + since |

例: He　left　town　　in 1980
　　主　過去式　　　明確時間副詞
　　and I haven't seen him since.
　　　　　　現在完成式
　　(一九八〇年他離城後，我便没再看到他。)

(3) 做介系詞用，之後加明確的時間名詞做受詞，亦可用動名詞做受詞。

例: I have been studying English since moving
　　　現在完成進行式　　　　　　　介　　動名詞
　　here in 1971.
　　(一九七一年搬到這裡後，我便一直唸英文。)

　　I have been studying English since
　　　　　　　　　　　　　　　　　　介
　　|1971.　　|
　　|Friday.　|
　　明確的時間名詞
　　(自從 一九七一年／星期五 以後，我便一直唸英文。)

比較: I have been studying English since 10
　　　years. (×, ten years 不是確定的時間名詞。)

改正: I have been studying English since 10
　　　years ago. (○)

注意:
since 之前亦可用副詞 ever 修飾。

例: Ever since he came here, he has been
　　getting along well with Mary.
　　(自從他來這裡後，便和瑪莉處得很好。)

　　He has stopped learning English ever
　　since five years ago.

（自五年前，他便停止學英文。）

He failed the exam two days ago and has
felt discouraged ever since.
（兩天之前他考試被當，從此便洩了氣。）

d. after　　之後

after 做副詞時亦譯成『之後』，但與 since 做副詞時不同的是：since 修飾完成式，而 after 則修飾過去式，此時等於 later 或 afterwards。

例: He fell ill on Monday and died three days
　　after.
　　later.
　　afterwards.
（他星期一生病，三天後就死了。）

Soon after, he moved to the United States.
（不久之後，他便搬去美國。）

The war ended in 1945, and they lived happily
ever after.
（戰爭於一九四五年結束，從此他們便快樂地生活著。）

6. quite　　十分地
   rather　　倒蠻……地
   此二字可修飾原級之副詞或形容詞

例: He is quite old.
　　　　　　　 adj.
（他很老了。）

He is rather old.
　　　　　　 adj.
（他相當老了。）

He studies <u>quite</u> <u>hard</u>.
　　　　　　　　　adv.

(他相當用功。)

但修飾形容詞 + 名詞時:

He is <u>a quite good</u> student. (×)

He is <u>quite a good</u> student. (○)
(他是個相當不錯的學生。)

They are <u>quite good</u> students. (○)
(他們是相當好的學生。)

He is <u>rather an old</u> man. (○)
(他是個相當老的人。)

They are <u>rather old</u> men.
(他們相當老了。)

7 . some day, one day, the other day, another day

a. some day　　將來總有一天 (用於未來式)
例: Keep on working hard, and <u>some day</u> you'll be successful.
(要不斷用功, 那麼將來總有一天你會成功。)

b. one day　　某日 (= the other day, 用於過去式);
　　　　　　　將來總有一天 (= some day, 用於未來式)

例: I saw him downtown <u>one day</u>.
過去式
(有一天我在城裡看到他。)

<u>One day</u> you'll be sorry for what you've done.
未來式

（總有一天你會後悔自己的所做所爲。）

c. the other day　　前些時候（用於過去式）

例: I went to Kenting National Park for a visit
　　過去式
　　the other day.
（前些天我到墾丁國家公園玩了一趟。）

d. some other day　　改天（用於未來式）

例: I'm busy now, I'll visit you some other day.
　　　　　　　　　　　未來式
（我現在很忙，改天再去拜訪你。）

8. so much so that　　如此……以致
談這個句構之前，雄雄老師先請同學看這個句子：

He is angry — so angry that he wants to kill the
rival that has stolen his girlfriend.
（他很火大——火大得要殺掉搶走他女友的情敵。）

這個句子文法是對的，但美中不足的是 angry 用了兩次，
就修辭的眼光來看，本句犯了重覆的毛病，爲補救這個缺
點，我們可用 much so 代替 angry，而形成下列的標準
句構：

He is angry — so much so that he wants to kill the
rival that has stolen his girlfriend.

於是，我們得了這樣的概念：
much so 可在 so...that 句構中代替前面已提及的副詞或
形容詞，以避免重覆。

例: 代替副詞

He studies <u>hard</u> — <u>so much so</u> (原爲 hard) <u>that</u>
　　　　　　adv.

he is sure to pass the exam.
(他很用功——用功得一定會考及格。)

　代替形容詞:
　She is <u>beautiful</u> — <u>so much so</u> (原爲 beautiful)
　　　　　　adj.

that I'm crazy about her.
(她很美——美得令我爲她發狂。)

9. somewhat, somehow, anyhow

a. somewhat　　有一點兒
　　該字爲一般副詞，使用時通常置於<u>形容詞</u>或<u>副詞</u>之前以
　　供修飾。

　例: It's <u>somewhat</u> <u>cold</u> today.
　　　　　　adv.　　adj.

　= It's │ a little │ cold today.
　　　　 │ more or less │
　(今天有點冷。)

　He did the work <u>somewhat</u> <u>carelessly</u>.
　　　　　　　　　　adv.　　　adv.

　(他這件事做得有些粗心。)

b. somehow　　不知怎的 (= for some unknown reason);
　　　　　　　設法 (= by some means)
　　表『不知怎的』時做獨立副詞，通常置於句首，修飾全句。

例: He is nice; <u>somehow</u> <u>I don't like him.</u>
　　　　　　　adv.

（他人不錯，不知怎的，我就是不喜歡他。）

表『設法』時，做一般副詞，修飾句中<u>動詞</u>，通常置於<u>句尾</u>。

例: We must <u>find</u> the money <u>somehow</u>.
　　　　　　vt.　　　　　　　adv.

（我們必須設法找到那筆錢。）

c. anyhow　　以任何方式 (= in any way);
　　　　　　　不管如何 (= at any rate)

表『以任何方式』時，anyhow 爲一般副詞，修飾句中<u>動詞</u>，通常置於<u>句尾</u>。

例: The doors were locked and the windows (were)
　　shut; we couldn't <u>get into</u> the building <u>anyhow</u>.
　　　　　　　　　　　vt. 片語　　　　　　　　　adv.

（門鎖著窗也關著，我們無法進入這大樓。）

表『不管如何』時，anyhow 爲獨立副詞，通常置於<u>句首</u>，之後有逗點，修飾<u>整個主要子句</u>。

例: | Anyhow,　　| we can try.
　　| Anyway,　　|
　　| At any rate,|

（不管怎樣，我們可以試試看。）

10. enough　adj. 充份的 &
　　　　　　　adv. 足可以

enough 不論做形容詞或副詞，其後通常接:
不定詞 to + 原形動詞，或 for + 名詞。

a. 形容詞: 此時 enough 表『充份的』，修飾名詞通常置
　　於該名詞前亦可置於其後。

例: He has <u>enough</u> <u>money</u> │ to buy the car.
　　　　　adj.　　n. │ <u>for</u> the car.

= He has <u>money</u> <u>enough</u> │ to buy the car.
　　　　　　　　　 │ <u>for</u> the car.

（他有足夠的錢買車。）

b. 副詞: 此時 enough 表『足可以』，修飾形容詞或副詞，
　　要置於該副詞或形容詞之後，不可置於其前。

例: He is <u>good</u> <u>enough</u> │ for the position.
　　　　 adj.　adv. │ <u>to fill</u> the position.

（他好得足以擔任此職位。）

He is <u>enough</u> <u>good</u> for the position. (×)

He ran <u>fast</u> <u>enough</u> to catch the train. (○)
　　　　adv.　adv.

（他跑得飛快趕上了火車。）

He ran <u>enough</u> <u>fast</u> to catch the train. (×)

11. likely, probably, possibly 可能地

例: He will (very, most) likely come.
（很有可能他會來。）

＊likely 做副詞時，通常之前添加 very 或 most 加以修飾

She will probably leave.

（她可能將要離開。）

They will possibly help him.
（他們可能會幫他。）

但 likely 亦可作形容詞，其用法如下：

He is likely to come. （○）
（他可能會來。）

He is probable to come. （×，probable 不能修飾人）

He is possible to come. （×，理由同上）

改正: It is possible for him to come. （○）
= It is │possible│
　　　　│likely │ that he will come. （○）
　　　　│probable│

1 2. Short Response （簡應句）: 你是……，我也是。你不是……，
　　 我也不是。

　　a. 肯定句用 so 或 too，so 前之 and 可省略。

　　例: be 動詞:
　　　　主詞與 be 動詞倒裝。

　　　　He <u>is</u> nice, (and) so <u>is she</u>.
　　　　　　　　　　　　= and <u>she is</u>, too.
　　　　（他人很好，她也很好。）
　　　　He <u>was</u> going home, (and) so <u>was she</u>.
　　　　　　　　　　　　　　= and <u>she was</u>, too.
　　　　（他即將回家，她也是。）

　　　　助動詞:
　　　　主詞與助動詞倒裝。

He <u>will</u> come, (and) so <u>will she</u>.
= and <u>she will</u>, too.
(他要來，她也要來。)

He <u>has</u> gone, (and) so <u>has she</u>.
= and <u>she has</u>, too.
(他走了，她也走了。)

　一般動詞:
主詞與 do, does, did 倒裝。

He <u>came</u>, (and) so <u>did she</u>.
= and <u>she did</u>, too.
(他來了，她也來了。)

He <u>has</u> a book, (and) so <u>does she</u>.
= and <u>she does</u>, too.
(他有書，她也有。)

注意:
在對話中，兩句指的是同一人時，不論句子是肯定句
或否定句，均用 so 引導，且句子不倒裝。

例: A: "He is stupid."
B: "So he is." = "Indeed he is."
A:『他很蠢。』
B:『他的確很蠢。』

A: "You can't do it."
B: "So I can't."
A:『你不會做這事。』
B:『我的確不會。』

b. 否定句用 neither (或 nor) 或 either。
neither 為副詞，故 and 不可省略，但 nor 為連接詞，
前面不必置 and。

例: be 動詞:
主詞與 be 動詞倒裝。

He isn't nice, and neither is she.
　　　　　　　　= nor is she. (nor 爲連接詞，故其
　　　　　　　　　　　　前不加 and)
　　　　　　　　= and she isn't, either.
(他不好，她也不好。)

He wasn't going home, and neither was she.
　　　　　　　　　　= nor was she.
　　　　　　　　　　= and she wasn't, either.
(他没回家，她也没回家。)

助動詞:
主詞與助動詞倒裝:
He won't come, and neither will she.
　　　　　= nor will she.
　　　　　= and she won't, either.
(他不來，她也不來。)

He hasn't gone, and neither has she.
　　　　　　= nor has she.
　　　　　　= and she hasn't, either.
(他没去，她也没去。)

一般動詞:
主詞與 do, does, did 倒裝:
He never tells a lie, and neither does she.
　　　　　　　　= nor does she.
　　　　　　　　= and she doesn't, either.
(他絕不說謊，她也絕不說謊。)

He has no book, and neither does she.
(或 He doesn't have any book)
　　　　　= nor does she.

= and she <u>doesn't</u>, either.
（他沒有書，她也沒有。）

注意：
also 只能用在肯定句中，置於 be 動詞之後，或一般
動詞之前。

例： He is kind, and she <u>is also</u> kind.
（他很親切，她也是。）
He has a pen, and she <u>also has</u> a pen.
（他有一支筆，她也有。）

3. 經常使用的『名詞 + 介詞 + 名詞』副詞片語：

hand in hand	（手拉著手）
side by side	（並肩）
shoulder to shoulder	（並肩）
arm in arm	（臂挽著臂）
word for word	（逐字地）
day by day	（天天）
night after night	（夜夜）
little by little	（漸漸）
one by one	（一個一個地）
one after another	（陸續地）
face to face	（面對面地）

例： They walked hand in hand down the road.
（他們手牽手地在路上走。）

They came in one after another.
（他們陸續地走進來。）

4. not 要置於不定詞片詞，分詞，及動名詞之前。

例： Since I have much work to do, I decide <u>not to</u>
go on a trip. （○）

（由於有很多事要辦，我決定不去旅行。）

He pretended <u>to not</u> know me. (×)
He pretended <u>not to</u> know me. (○)
（他假裝不認識我。）

<u>Having not</u> finished the work, I decided to stay.
(×)
<u>Not having</u> finished the work, I decided to stay.
（工作沒完成，我決定留下來。）

He is disappointed at <u>not having</u> finished the
work. (○)
（他很失望沒把工作完成。）

15. 助動詞 + 副詞 + 本動詞

例：I <u>can always count on</u> you for advice. (○)
（我始終可以指望你給我忠告。）

I <u>have never seen</u> him before. (○)
I <u>never have seen</u> him before. (劣)
（我從沒見過他。）

16. 副詞修飾被動語態時，置於過去分詞之前。

例：His speech was <u>well presented</u>.
（他演說得很好。）

That case was <u>completely settled down</u>.
（那件事完全解決了。）

That project had <u>been studied very carefully</u>
before it was handed over to the boss. (劣，應
為 very carefully studied)
（那份計劃在交給老闆之前，曾被很仔細地研究過。）

17. more than 與倍數的關係：
    more than 應置於倍數之前。

    例: He has three times as much money as you do.
    (他的錢是你的三倍。)

    He has <u>more than</u> three times as much money as
    you do.
    (他的錢超過你的三倍。)

    He has three times more than as much money as
    you do. (×)

    Our income has <u>more than</u> doubled in one year.
    (一年之內我們的收入增加了一倍多。)

18. more than 與 over 的關係;
    over 做介詞表『超過』時，可用 more than 代替。

    例: He has stayed here over a year.
     = He has stayed here more than a year.
    (他已待在此地一年多。)

    He has stayed here <u>more than</u> <u>over</u> a year. (×)
    He has stayed here <u>much</u> <u>over</u> a year. (×, much
    應刪除)

    Over five students are here.
     = More than five students are here.
    (這裡的學生有五人以上。)

19. 避免雙重比較，即 more richer, more better 等等。

    例: She is more <u>beautiful</u> than Mary. (○)
    (她比瑪莉還美。)

She is <u>better</u> than Mary. (○)
（她比瑪莉好。）

She is much <u>better</u> than Mary. (○)
（她比瑪莉好很多。）

She is <u>more better</u> than Mary. (×，因 better 已經
是比較級，不可再被比較級副詞 more 修飾。)

People in Taiwan lead a much <u>richer</u> life than
those in Red China. (○)
（台灣人民比大陸人民的生活富裕。）

People in Taiwan lead a much <u>richer</u> life <u>more</u>
than those in Red China. (×)

２０. 避免雙重否定

例: He has <u>never</u> been to Japan before. (○)

He hasn't never been to Japan before. (×)

He hasn't ever been to Japan before. (○, not
ever = never)
（他從來沒去過日本。）

You'll have to hurry up; we have <u>hardly no</u> time
left. (×)
You'll have to hurry up; we have <u>hardly any</u> time
left. (○)
（你必須快點，我們沒時間了。）

注意:
scarcely = hardly = almost not, 爲否定副詞, 不可與 no
或 not 並用。

例: He can scarcely do this work. (○)
（他幾乎不會做這工作。）

He can <u>not</u> scarcely do this work. (×)

He has | hardly | <u>any</u> money. (○)
　　　 | almost not |
（他幾乎沒有錢。）
He has hardly no money. (×)

2 1. 關係副詞 when, why, how, where

例: This is the time <u>when</u> we should set out.
　　　　　　　　　 ↑_____| (= at which)
（該是我們出發的時候了。）

This is the reason <u>why</u> he was late.
　　　　　　　　　 ↑_____|(= for which)
（這就是為何他遲到的理由。）

This is the way <u>how</u> he succeeded.
　　　　　　　 ↑____|(= in which)
（這就是他成功的方法。）

That is the place <u>where</u> I was born.
　　　　　　　　 ↑_____|(= in which)
（那是我出生的地方。）

This is the reason <u>because</u> he was late. (×)

I came yesterday <u>where</u> it was raining heavily.
(×, yesterday 為時間，故 where 應改為 when。)

That is the city <u>how</u> he lives. (×, city 為地方
，故 how 應改為 where。)

注意:

關係副詞亦可作複合關係副詞, 代替前面的名詞(先行詞), 是故上述各例亦可改爲:

This is <u>when</u> we should start.
　　　　(= the time when)

This is <u>where</u> I live.
　　　　(= the place where)

22. 有些代名詞可作副詞用

The destination is too far away; I can't walk <u>that</u> far.　　　　　　　　　　　　　　　　　　　　　(= so)
(目的地太遠了; 我走不到那麼遠。)

"How big is the bear?" "It is about <u>that</u> big."
(『熊有多大?』 『大概有那麼大。』)

23. think, hope, believe, be afraid, imagine 等動詞之後加 so 代替肯定句, 加 not 則代替否定句。

例: "Is he nice?"
　　"Yes, I think so." (so = that he is nice)
　　"No, I think not." (not = that he is not nice)
　　(『他人好嗎?』)
　　(『我想他是好人。』 / 『我看他不是好人。』)

　　"Will he come?"
　　"I'm afraid not." (not = that he will not come)
　　"I'm afraid so." (so = that he will come)
　　(『他會來嗎?』)
　　(『我恐怕他不會來。 /『恐怕他會來哦!』)

24. 獨立分詞 speaking 用副詞修飾, 形成 strictly speaking (嚴格地說), frankly speaking (坦白地說), broadly

speaking (概括地說)。

例: Strictly speaking, he is wrong.
Strict speaking, he is wrong. (×)
(嚴格地說，他是不對的。)

2 5. all (三人以上一起)，both (兩人一起)

例: John, Paul, and Peter will all come here tomorrow
to celebrate Jack's birthday.
(約翰、保羅和彼得明天都要來這裡慶祝傑克的生日。)

These five students are all good.
(這五位都是好學生。)

The two candidates are both qualified for this job.
(這兩位候選人都有資格做此工作。)

He and I will all go to Taichung tomorrow.
(×，all 應改爲 both。)
(他和我明天都要去台中。)

2 6. 容易混淆的副詞
a. close (近)，closely (仔細地,嚴密地)

例: I live close to his house.
= I live near his house.
(我住在他家附近。)

Watch him closely.
(好好盯著他。)

b. most (最)，mostly (大部份，大都)

例: Of all the books here, I like this one most.
(在這些書中，我最喜歡這本。)

These books are mostly out of date.
(這些書大部份都過時了。)

c. near (近), nearly (= almost, 幾乎)

例: He lives near, not far.
(他住附近，不在遠處。)

He was nearly drowned. (他差點淹死。)

注意:
near 若當介詞，其後加動名詞時，表『幾乎』，但不得以
nearly 代替。

例: He | came | near being drowned.
        | was |

= He | came | close to being drowned.
       | was |

= He was nearly drowned.

He came nearly being drowned.(×)

d. high ⎤
   deep ⎬ 表實際空間(可以用尺量)的 → 高
   wide ⎦   → 深
                                       ↘ 寬

   highly ⎤
   deeply ⎬ 表程度而不指空間的 → 高
   widely ⎦   → 深
                               ↘ 寬

例: The plane flew high in the sky.
(飛機高高在天上飛著。)
The plane flew highly in the sky. (×)

He was highly praised. (○)
(他大大地受到讚揚。)

We spoke highly of him. (○)
(我們褒揚他。)

We think highly of him. (○)
(我們看重他。)

He was <u>high</u> spoken of. (×, high 應改爲 highly)

He jumped deep into the river. (○)
(他深深跳入水中。)

He was deep hurt. (×, and 應改爲 deeply)

27. greatly 與 highly 之區別
   a. greatly 表『大量地，大大地』。

   例: He was greatly surprised.
   (他大大地吃了一驚。)

   The number of traffic accidents has increased greatly.
   (車禍次數大幅增加。)

   b. highly 表『高高地』，通常與『表揚』『獎勵』等動詞並用

   例: He is highly <u>praised</u>.
   (他被捧得很高。)

   We think highly of him.
   (我們很看重他。)

Exercise

I. 請選出一個正確的答案:

1. Anna didn't like our new roommate, and _____.
   (A) I don't too
   (B) neither I did
   (C) neither did I
   (D) I didn't also

2. The population of many Alaskan towns has _____ doubled during the past three years.
   (A) much than
   (B) as more as than
   (C) as more than
   (D) more than

3. _____ he began working in the chemical plant, he experienced pain when he breathed.
   (A) Shortly before
   (B) Not long after
   (C) No sooner than
   (D) No longer

4. How many brand-new cars there are! Automobile production in the last ten years has increased _____.
   (A) highly
   (B) infinitely
   (C) in the large scale
   (D) greatly

5. Bill wasn't happy about the delay, and _____.
   (A) I was neither
   (B) I wasn't, either
   (C) neither I was
   (D) either was I

6. The second hurricane struck the coastal states _____ three days after the first one.
   (A) during
   (B) just
   (C) not as much as
   (D) not as little as

7. Who's that good-looking girl Frank is dancing with?
   I _____ her before.

(A) never had seen   (B) had never seen

(C) saw never   (D) never saw

8 . When Arthur applied for a job, Professor Adams was
able to recommend him _____.
(A) very highly   (B) with superb notices
(C) greatly   (D) with high regard

9 . Children learn very quickly. When they learn about
a new subject, they often _____.
(A) become too interested   (B) very much are interested
(C) become much interested   (D) are interested very much

1 0 . The price of oil, as we know, has _____ doubled in the
past three years.
(A) larger than   (B) more than
(C) as great as   (D) as many as

1 1 . John is very diligent. But his pay is not _____ for
his work.
(A) enough good   (B) good enough
(C) as good enough   (D) good as enough

1 2 . You didn't hear us come in last night. That's good.
We tried _____ noisy.
(A) to be not   (B) not to be
(C) not be   (D) be not

1 3 . This old desk isn't _____ to sell, but maybe we could
give it to someone.
(A) goodly enough   (B) good enough
(C) good as enough   (D) enough good

1 4 . She overslept and was _____ late that she missed the bus.
(A) so   (B) too   (C) much   (D) very

15. Eric nearly always wins the science award. That's
    because his projects are _____ .
    (A) extremely presented well
    (B) well presented extremely
    (C) presented well extremely
    (D) extremely well presented

16. Betty got married last week; _____ that she would get
    married so young.
    (A) I never dream   (B) Never do I have dreamed
    (C) Do I never dream   (D) I never dreamed

17. My brother seldom does his homework in the morning.
    _____ .
    (A) So does John   (B) John is too
    (C) John doesn't too   (D) Nor does John

18. Take an umbrella when you go to Seattle, for it rains
    _____ there.
    (A) frequently   (B) as frequent
    (C) most of times   (D) much time

19. I walked 8 miles today; I never guessed that I could
    walk _____ far.
    (A) that   (B) this   (C) such   (D) as

20. Prices for bikes at that store can run _____ $250.
    (A) as high as   (B) so high to
    (C) as high to   (D) so high as

Ⅱ. 請選出錯誤的劃線部份:
21. Many of the observations <u>made by</u> Leonardo a little
                             A
    <u>greater</u> than 400 years ago <u>about</u> the movement of
      B   C
    birds' wings <u>have been verified</u> by modern photos.
                    D

2 2. The state legislature has approved the construction
A
of a completely self-contained paper-recycling
B
plant that will produce hardly no harmful waste
C   D
materials.

2 3. Of all the Christmas toys the boy saw in the window,
A   B
the thing he wanted more was a new bicycle.
C   D

2 4. Rain clouds and smoke caused by pollution look

so much alike that one cannot hardly tell
A   B
the difference between the two of them.
C   D

2 5. The large ship sailed very good in any weather, never
A   B
requiring more than one man at the wheel.
C   D

2 6. A carefully trained observer can discover details very
A   B
easy although others never see them.
C   D

2 7. She spoke so indistinct that we did not know whether
A   B
we were to precede or follow the procession.
C   D

2 8. A Cezanne painting was recently sold at an auction
A B

for <u>much over</u> the <u>initially</u> announced price.
      C   D

29. Interest <u>in</u> automatic data processing has <u>grown</u> <u>rapid</u>
           A   B   C

    <u>since</u> the first large calculators were introduced
     D

    in 1950.

30. Today divorce is <u>not longer</u> regarded <u>as</u> a disgrace
                      A   B

    <u>nor</u> a tragedy, <u>not even</u> a failure.
     C   D

標準答案：1.(C)　2.(D)　3.(B)　4.(D)　5.(B)　6.(B)　7.(D)
        8.(A)　9.(C) 10.(B) 11.(B) 12.(B) 13.(B) 14.(A)
       15.(D) 16.(D) 17.(D) 18.(A) 19.(A) 20.(A) 21.(B)
       22.(D) 23.(D) 24.(B) 25.(B) 26.(C) 27.(A) 28.(C)
       29.(C) 30.(A)

習題解答：
    1. and neither did I.
     = nor did I.
     = and I didn't, either.

    2. more than 在此作副詞用，修飾動詞 doubled。

    3. shortly before　　　就在……之前
       not long after　　　在……之後沒有多久

    4. greatly　　　大幅地
       in the large scale 應改爲 on a large scale。

    5. 與第一題同理。

    6. (A) during 要接限定的時間，例如 during those three

days, during that period。

(B) just three days after the first one 就在第一個
颱風之後三天。

(C)(D) not as much as 及 not as little as 只能修
飾不可數名詞，但 three days 是可數名詞，不能被
much, little 修飾。

7. 過去完成式不能單獨存在，一定要配合另一過去式子句。
例: I had finished my job. (×)
I had finished my job before you came. (○)

8. (B) 無此片語
(C) recommend (推薦)並非表『量』的概念，故不能用
greatly。
(D) with high regard 為副詞片語，表『尊敬地』，此處與
語意不合。

9. (A) become too interested (變得太有趣而不能……)
(B) very much 應置於 interested 之前。
(C) much 修飾過去分詞是正確的。
(D) very much 應置於 interested 之前。

10. 與第二題同理

11. enough 作副詞時，一定要置於其所修飾之形容或副詞之後。

12. 不定詞片語與 not 合用時，not 一定要置於不定詞之前。

13. 與第十一題同理。

14. so...that...   如此……以致於……

15. 副詞修飾被動語態時，一定要置於過去分詞之前。

16. 本句應用過去式 I never dreamed...表現在已知，但
當時未想到。

如使用現在完成式時應爲 I have never dreamed...
或 Never have I dreamed...

１７．與第一題同理

１８．動詞應用副詞修飾
　　(B) 形容詞
　　(C) 若改爲 most of the time(大部分時間)就對了
　　(D) much time『不少時間』通常作 spend, have 的受詞。
　　　　例: I spend much time practising English
　　　　　　every day.
　　　　　　Don't worry; we still have much time.

１９．that far
　　 = so far

２０．as high as　　　高達……
　　本片語中的 as 不可用 so 來代換。

２１．(B) greater 應改爲 more, 表時間。

２２．(D) hardly no 應改爲 hardly any = almost not any =
　　　almost no

２３．(D) more 應爲 most, 三者以上的比較。

２４．(B) cannot hardly 應改爲 can hardly。

２５．(B) very good 應改爲 very well 以修飾動詞 sailed。

２６．(C) easy 應改爲 easily 以修飾動詞 discover。

２７．(A) indistinct 應改爲 indistinctly (不清楚地) 以修飾
　　　動詞 spoke。

２８．(C) much over 應改爲 over 或 more than。

29. (C) rapid 應改為 rapidly，以修飾 grown。

30. (A) not longer 應改為 no longer。

第九章
倒裝句構

概說:

　　倒裝句是英語特有的句型。其目的是藉由句中某些詞類的倒置，可用以強調整個句子的語氣。偶而在一篇文章出現倒裝的句構，可以使平淡的句子變得生動活潑。一般常出現的倒裝句構有下列五種:

1. 否定倒裝句:

　　例: I have never seen such a pretty girl as she (is).
　　→ Never have I seen such a pretty girl as she.
　　(我從沒見過像她這麼美的女孩。)

2. so/such　倒裝句:

　　例: She is so kind that she deserves all my respect.
　　→ So kind is she that she deserves all my respect.
　　(她人很好，值得我尊敬。)

3. 地方副詞倒裝句:

　　例: A boy stood there.
　　→ There stood a boy.
　　(那兒站著一個男孩。)

4. 完全倒裝句:

　　例: He who works hard is respectable.
　　→ Respectable is he who works hard.
　　(努力工作的人值得尊敬。)

5. as 取代 though 的倒裝句：

例: Though he is nice, I dislike him.
→ <u>Nice</u> <u>as</u> he is, I dislike him.
(他人雖然好，我卻不喜歡他。)

　　以上所列的倒裝句結構變化並不複雜，但同學在學習英語的過程中，不曾嘗試過自行整理這些句型，以致在寫作的時候，要不就不會運用，要不就犯錯。對參與各類英語考試的同學而言，本章至為重要，因為倒裝句是出題先生們極易考的一個項目。因此同學在閱讀本章時，一定要有無比的耐心，細嚼慢嚥。雄哥保證你一定能完全吸收，使自己的英語程度又往前邁進一大步！

第一節　否定倒裝句

否定倒裝句就是將否定副詞，否定副詞片語，否定副詞子句移至句首的倒裝句。使用此類倒裝句要注意兩個重點：

a. 何為否定副詞、否定副詞片語、否定副詞子句？

b. 如何倒裝？

我們且一一分項說明。

1. 常用的否定副詞：
never (從不), hardly (=scarcely　幾乎不), rarely (很少),
seldom (很少), little (幾乎不)

常用的否定副詞片語：
by no means(絕對不), in no way (絕對不), on no account
(絕對不), under no circumstances (絕對不), in no
situation (絕對不)

常用的否定副詞子句(一共只有三種句型，很好背！)

```
not until he came      (直到他來)
only when he came      (只有到他來的時候)
only after he came     (只有到他來之後)
```

2 . 如何倒裝：
先將否定副詞，否定副詞片語或否定副詞子句移至句首，再檢查原句構主詞之後的動詞。

a. be 動詞
主詞之後有 be 動詞時，be 動詞與主詞要倒裝。

例: He is never happy.
　　　　否定副詞
→ Never is he happy.
　　(他從不快樂。)

He is hardly ever quiet.
　　　　否定副詞
→ Hardly is he ever quiet.
　　(他一點也安靜不下來。)

You are by no means the person we need.
　　　　否定副詞片語
→ By no means are you the person we need.
　　(你絕非我們需要的人。)

I was not aware of it until he came.
　　　　　　　　　　　　副詞子句
→ Not until he came was I aware of it.
　　否定副詞子句
　　(直到他來，我才發覺這件事。)

He is happy only when Mary is with him.
　　　　　　　否定副詞子句
→ Only when Mary is with him is he happy.
　　否定副詞子句

（只有瑪莉和他在一起時，他才快樂。）

b. 助動詞
主詞之後有助動詞時，助動詞與主詞要倒裝。

例: He can <u>hardly</u> sing.
　　　　　否定副詞
→ <u>Hardly</u> can he sing.
　（他一點也不會唱歌。）

　He <u>has</u> <u>never</u> done it before.
　　　　　否定副詞
→ <u>Never</u> <u>has he</u> done it before.
　（他從來沒做過這事。）

　He <u>can</u> do it <u>under no circumstances</u>.
　　　　　　　　　　　　否定副詞片語
→ <u>Under no circumstances</u> <u>can he</u> do it.
　（他絕不做此事。）

　He <u>will</u> <u>not</u> do it <u>until Mary offers to help</u>.
　　　　　　　　　　　　副詞子句
→ <u>Not until Mary offers to help</u> <u>will he</u> do it.
　　　否定副詞子句
　（直到瑪莉主動幫忙，他才做這事。）

c. 一般動詞:
主詞之後有動詞時，先在主詞之前按動詞時態以及主詞
人稱之不同，分置 do, does 或 did，再將動詞變成
原形動詞。

例: He　　seldom　　　　sings.
　　　　否定副詞　現在式第三人稱單數
→ <u>Seldom</u> <u>does</u> he sing.
　　　　　　　　　原形 v.
　（他很少唱歌。）

He little knew that Mary's English could be
　　　否定副詞 過去式

so good.

→ Little did he know that Mary's English could be
　　　　　　　　　原形 v.

so good.
(他絕沒想到瑪莉的英文如此地好。)

We by no means understand what he says.
　　否定副詞片語 現在式第一人稱複數

→ By no means do we understand what he says.
(我們無法了解他說的話。)

They didn't know the truth until Mary came.
　　　　　　　　　　　　　　　　副詞子句

→ Not until Mary came did they know the truth.
　　否定副詞子句　　　　　　原形 v.
(直到瑪莉來了，他們才了解實情。)

3. only + 介系詞片語
此可視爲否定副詞片語，置於句首時，亦採倒裝句。

例：Only by doing so you can succeed. (×)
　　否定副詞片語

→ Only by doing so can you succeed. (○)
(只有這麼做你才會成功。)

Only with his help I will be able to tide over
否定副詞片語
the difficulties. (×)

→ Only with his help will I be able to tide over
the difficulties. (○)
(有了他的幫助，我才能克服困難。)

| Only at that time | I left. (×)
| Only then

→ |Only at that time| did I leave. (○)
　 |Only then　　　　|
　（到那時我才離開。）

4. not only...but (also)　　　不僅……而且
 = not merely...but (also)
 = not only...but...as well
 = not merely...but...as well

注意:
a. 本片語可用以連接對等的單字、片語、子句

例: 單字: Not only I but (also) he is wrong.
　　　　　　　　　　　主詞
　　　（不但是我，連他也錯了。）

　　　　She is not only kind but graceful as
　　　　　　　　　　　　形容詞
　　　　well.
　　　（她人不但親切而且優雅。）

片語: I came not only to see you but to say
　　　　　　　　　　不定詞片語
　　　good-bye to you.
　　　（我來不僅是為了見你，也是來跟你道別的。）

　　　　He was fired not only because of
　　　　　　　　　　　　　副詞片語
　　　laziness but because of failure to
　　　　　　　　　　　　副詞片語
　　　meet my requirement.
　　　（他被開除不僅是因為懶惰，還因為無法達到
　　　我的要求。）

子句：He was fired <u>not merely</u> <u>because he was</u>
副詞子句

<u>lazy</u> <u>but</u> <u>because he failed to meet my</u>
副詞子句

requirement.

(他被開除不僅是因為懶惰，還因為無法達到我的要求。)

b. 本片語亦可連接對等的主要子句，但由於 not only 置於句首，視為否定副詞，第一個主要子句要倒裝。but also 僅為連接詞，故其後的第二個主要子句不須倒裝，但 also 則一定要省略，或移至句中。亦可將 also 省略後而在句尾處加 as well 。

例：<u>Not only she can sing</u>, <u>but also she can dance</u>. (×)
主要子句　　　　　　　主要子句

→ Not only <u>can she</u> sing, <u>but</u> she can (also) dance. (○)

或 Not only <u>can she</u> sing, <u>but</u> she can dance <u>as well</u>. (○)

(她不僅會唱歌而且還會跳舞。)

Before I left, <u>not only</u> I had closed the door, <u>but also</u> I had cleaned the room. (×)

→ Before I left, not only <u>had I</u> closed the door, <u>but</u> I had (also) cleaned the room. (○)

或 Before I left, not only <u>had I</u> closed the door, <u>but</u> I had cleaned the room <u>as well</u>. (○)

(我離開之前，不但關了門還打掃了房間。)

5. not + a + 單數可數名詞　　連一個……都沒有
本片語若做及物動詞的受詞時，亦可移至句首，採倒裝句構。

例：I did <u>not</u> see <u>any soul</u> (= man) over there.
→ <u>Not a soul</u> <u>did I</u> see over there.
(我在那兒一個人也沒看到。)

I was not able to discover any clue to the murder.
→ Not a clue was I able to discover to the murder.
（這件謀殺案我連一點蛛絲馬跡也沒法找到。）

6 . hardly, scarcely
這兩個副詞，因爲是否定副詞，故置於句首時，句子要倒裝。
兩字意思相同，均譯成『幾乎不』，用法亦相同。

例: Hardly he can do it. (×)
→ Hardly can he do it. (○)
（他無法做這事。）

Scarcely he was able to finish the job on schedule. (×)
→ Scarcely was he able to finish the job on schedule. (○)
（他無法照進度完成此工作。）

注意:
| scarcely |
| hardly | + any + 名詞
= almost not + any + 名詞
= almost no + 名詞
此時若做主詞，置於句首，不可採倒裝句構。

例: Scarcely did any student pass the exam. (×)
→ Scarcely any student passed the exam. (○)
= Almost no student passed the exam. (○)
（幾乎沒有一個學生通過考試。）

Hardly did anyone of us know the answer. (×)
→ Hardly anyone of us knew the answer. (○)
= Almost no one of us knew the answer. (○)
（我們沒有一個知道答案。）

但：$\left|\begin{array}{l}\text{scarcely}\\\text{hardly}\end{array}\right|$ + any + 名詞，若做受詞，置於句首時，
　　　　仍採倒裝句。

例: He has <u>hardly any money</u>. (○)
　→ <u>Hardly any money</u> <u>does</u> he <u>have</u>. (○)
　　（他一點錢也沒有。）

7. nowhere = in no place　　在任何地方都不……
此亦為否定副詞，置於句首要採倒裝句。

<u>Nowhere</u> I could find such a man. (×)
→ <u>Nowhere</u> <u>could</u> I find such a man. (○)
（這種人我到處都找不到。）

8. 表『一……就……』的句型：
此句型有下列幾種：

她一見到我就昏倒了。（大概是因為雄哥長得像條豬。）

a. 同時態的副詞子句：

　<u>As soon as</u> she saw me, she passed out.
= <u>Once</u> she saw me, she passed out.
= $\left|\begin{array}{l}\text{The instant}\\\text{The moment}\end{array}\right|$ she saw me, she passed out.
（她一看見我就昏了過去。）

有的字典亦列出下列的用法：

$\left|\begin{array}{l}\text{Immediately}\\\text{Instantly}\\\text{Directly}\end{array}\right|$ she saw me, she passed out.

此時 immediately, instantly, directly 視為副詞連接詞，
等於 as soon as。但這種用法已不常見於報章雜誌中，故同

學寫作時，不宜使用。

b. 介系詞 + $\begin{vmatrix} \text{Ving} \\ \text{N} \end{vmatrix}$：

$\begin{vmatrix} \text{Upon} \\ \text{On} \end{vmatrix}$ seeing me, she passed out.

注意：

upon 或 on 之後加名詞或動名詞時，亦表示『一……
就……』之意，係由 as soon as 引導的副詞子句變化
而成。使用時要注意下列事項：

as soon as 引導的副詞子句中，主詞若與主要子句的主詞
相同時，upon 或 on 之後加動名詞；主詞不同時，則副詞
子句中的主詞要變成所有格，置於 upon 或 on 之後，再
接動名詞或名詞。

例：同主詞：

As soon as I finished the job, I went home.
→ $\begin{vmatrix} \text{Upon} \\ \text{On} \end{vmatrix}$ finishing the job, I went home.
（我一做完工作就回家。）

不同主詞：

As soon as he arrived, I left.
→ $\begin{vmatrix} \text{Upon} \\ \text{On} \end{vmatrix}$ his arriving, I left.
或 $\begin{vmatrix} \text{Upon} \\ \text{On} \end{vmatrix}$ his arrival, I left.
（他一來我就走了。）

c. 否定倒裝的副詞子句：

(1) 此類句型一共有三種：

(a) no sooner...than...　　(沒有比……快多久)

(b) hardly...when(或before)...
(當……時，幾乎沒……)

(c) scarcely...before(或when)...
(在……之前，幾乎沒……)

均譯爲『一……就……』。

(2) 造句法：

她一見到我就昏倒了。

第一步：先造一個過去完成式的句子 表示先發生的動作：

She <u>had</u> seen me.

第二步：再造一個過去式的句子，表示後發生的動作：

She passed out.

第三步：兩句放在一起：

She had seen me, she passed out.

第四步：加入 no sooner...than...等連接詞

She had no sooner seen me than she passed out.

字面翻譯：她先見到我，沒有比她後來昏倒快多少。

· 實際翻譯：她一見到我就昏倒。

She had hardly seen me when she passed out.

字面翻譯：當她昏倒時，幾乎沒看到我。

實際翻譯：她一見到我就昏倒。

She had scarcely seen me before she passed out.

字面翻譯：在她昏倒之前，幾乎沒看到我。

實際翻譯：她一見到我就昏倒了。

＊ hardly 與 scarcely 均等於 almost not，故之後的 when 與 before 可以互換。

(3) 由於 no sooner, hardly, scarcely 均爲否定副詞，置於句首時，過去完成式助動詞 had 應與主詞倒裝。

No sooner had she seen me than she passed out.

Scarcely had she seen me before she passed out.

Hardly had she seen me when she passed out.

至此，我們應當對『一……就……』的句型完全了解。雄哥希望同學能多加使用，練就更好的寫作能力。

第二節 SO／SUCH倒裝句

在 so...that... 或 such...that... 的句構中，若將 so 或 such 及其所引導的詞類置於句首時，亦採倒裝句構。句法與否定倒裝句完全相同。

1. 句中有 be 動詞時，該 be 動詞與主詞倒裝

   例: He is <u>so helpful</u> that we all like him.
   → So helpful <u>is he</u> that we all like him.
   (他這麼幫忙，我們都喜歡他。)

   They <u>are such lazy students</u> that they have no hope of passing the exam.
   → Such lazy students <u>are they</u> that they have no hope of passing the exam.
   (他們是很懶惰的學生，沒希望通過考試。)

2. 句中有助動詞時，該助動詞與主詞倒裝

   例: He <u>has done so well</u> that he deserves our respect.
   → So well <u>has he</u> done that he deserves our respect.
   (他做得這麼好，值得我們尊敬。)

   He <u>can do such a difficult job</u> that he must be quite talented.
   → Such a difficult job <u>can he</u> do that he must be quite talented.
   (他能勝任這麼困難的工作，一定很有天賦。)

3. 句中若有動詞時不可直接倒裝，須在主詞之前先按該動詞時

態及人稱變化，分置 do, does 或 did，再將該動詞變成原
形動詞。

例: He came so late that he missed the train.
→ So late did he come that he missed the train.
(他太晚到，沒趕上火車。)

　He did such a wonderful job that he won our
　respect.
→ Such a wonderful job did he do that he won our
　respect.
(他做得如此地棒，贏得我們的尊敬。)

　She sings so well that she can make a good
　singer.
→ So well does she sing that she can make a good
　singer.
(她唱得這麼好，一定可以當個好歌手。)

第三節　地方副詞倒裝句

1 ．地方副詞(there, here)，或地方副詞片語(in the room, at the station, by the window)，置於句首，亦可形成倒裝句。唯倒裝的句法與前兩種倒裝句完全不同。此類倒裝句全按動詞的性質做變化，句型有三種：

第一型：主詞 ＋ 不及物動詞 ＋ │ 地方副詞　　│
　　　　　　　　　　　　　　　　│ 地方副詞片語│

　　→│ 地方副詞　　│ ＋ 不及物動詞 ＋ 主詞
　　　│ 地方副詞片語│

　　例：A girl sat │ there.
　　　　 s.　vi. │ 地方副詞
　　　　　　　　　│ by the door.
　　　　　　　　　│ 地方副詞片語

　　→│ There　　　│ sat a girl.
　　　│ By the door│ vi.　 s.
　　　（那兒／門邊 坐著一個女孩。）

　　　A book is on the desk.
　　　　 s.　vi.　地方副詞片語
　　→ On the desk is a book.
　　　　　　　　　 vi.　 s.
　　　（桌上有本書。）

　　　Mary stood in the doorway.
　　　 s.　 vi.　 地方副詞片語
　　→ In the doorway stood Mary.
　　　　　　　　　　 vi.　 s.
　　　（瑪莉站在門口。）

第二型：主詞 + be 動詞 + 過去分詞 + │地方副詞　　　│
　　　　　　　　　　　　　　　　　│地方副詞片語　│

→ │地方副詞　　　│ + be 動詞 + 過去分詞 + 主詞
　 │地方副詞片語　│

例：A man was locked behind the door.
　　　　　　be　 p.p. 　地方副詞片語
→ Behind the door was locked a man.
（門後鎖著一個人。）

A school is located there.
　　　　　be　p.p. 　地方副詞
→ There is located a school.
（那裡座落著一所學校。）

第三型：主詞 + be 動詞 + 現在分詞 + │地方副詞　　　│
　　　　　　　　　　　　　　　　　│地方副詞片語　│

→ 現在分詞+ │地方副詞　　　│ + be 動詞 + 主詞
　　　　　　 │地方副詞片語　│

例：A girl is singing over there.
　　　　　 be 現在分詞 地方副詞片語
→ Singing over there is a girl.
（或 Over there is singing a girl.）
（那兒有個女孩在唱歌。）

Mary and David were sitting in front of
　　　　　　　　　 be 　現在分詞 地方副詞片語
the gate.
→ Sitting in front of the gate were Mary and
David.
（或 In front of the gate were sitting
Mary and David.）
（瑪莉和大衛坐在大門前。）

2. 此類倒裝句中的主詞一定是普通名詞(a book, a man, the children...等)，或專有名詞(Mary, Peter...等)。若主詞<u>為代名詞(it, she, they...等)則不可採倒裝句</u>。也就是說<u>地方副詞仍可放在句首，但句子不倒裝</u>。至於地方副詞片語則不宜放在句首。

例: <u>He</u> stood <u>there</u>.
　　代名詞　　地方副詞
→ There stood <u>he</u>. (×)
→ There <u>he</u> stood. (○)
　(他站在那兒。)

　　He stood <u>in front of the house</u>.
　　　　　　　地方副詞片語
→ <u>In front of the house</u> stood he. (×)
→ <u>In front of the house</u> he stood. (劣)
　　地方副詞片語
→ He stood <u>in front of the house</u>. (佳)
　(他站在房子前面。)

例: <u>He</u> was locked <u>there</u>.
　　代名詞　　　　　地方副詞
→ There was locked <u>he</u>. (×)
→ There <u>he was locked</u>. (○)
　(他被鎖在那裡。)

　　He was locked <u>behind the door</u>.
　　　　　　　　地方副詞片語
→ <u>Behind the door</u> was locked he. (×)
→ <u>Behind the door</u> he was locked. (劣)
　　地方副詞片語
→ He was locked <u>behind the door</u>. (佳)

例: He was singing <u>there</u>.
　　　　　　　　　地方副詞
→ Singing there was <u>he</u>. (×)

→ There he was singing.(○)
　(他在那裡唱歌。)

　He was singing in the backyard.
　　　　　　　　　地方副詞片語
→ Singing in the backyard was he. (×)
→ He was singing in the backyard. (○)
　(他在後院裡唱歌。)

3．介副詞亦視爲地方副詞，置於句首，亦採完全相同的倒裝句
　。所謂介副詞，就是表場所的介系詞(如 in, out, down, up,
　off 等)。這些字之後有受詞時就稱介系詞，無受詞時就是介
　副詞(由介詞變成的副詞)。

　介詞：John walked in(to) the room.
　　　　　　　　　　介　　　　o.
　　　(約翰走進房間。)

　　　The boy looked out the window.
　　　　　　　　　　介　　　o.
　　　(這男孩向窗外看。)

　　　He came down the stairs.
　　　　　　　　介　　　o.
　　　(他走下樓。)

　　　He climbed up the mountain.
　　　　　　　　　介　　　o.
　　　(他爬上山。)

　　　He fell off the roof.
　　　(他從屋頂上摔下來。)

　介副詞：He walked in.
　　　　　　　　　　介副詞
　　　(他走進去。)

He looked <u>out</u>.
　　　　　　　　介副詞
(他往外看。)

He came <u>down</u>.
　　　　　　　　介副詞
(他走下來。)

He climbed <u>up</u>.
　　　　　　　　　介副詞
(他爬上去。)

倒裝方式：A boy <u>walked</u> <u>in</u>.
　　　　　　　　　　vi.
→ <u>In</u> walked a boy.
　　(一個男孩走了進來。)

The car <u>dashed</u> <u>off</u>.
　　　　　　　　　　　vi.
→ <u>Off</u> <u>dashed</u> the car.
　　(這輛車子飛馳而過。)

John <u>came</u> <u>down</u>.
　　　　　　　vi.
→ <u>Down</u> came John.
　　(約翰走了下來。)

注意：
a. 主詞爲代名詞時，不得採倒裝句構。

例：In <u>he</u> walked. (○)
　　　　代名詞
　　(他走進來。)

In walked he. (×)

Off they went. (○)
　　　代名詞
(他們走了。)

Off went they. (×)

b. away 為一地方副詞，用法相同。

例: John went away.
→ Away went John. (○)
(約翰走了。)

Away he went. (○)
　　　代名詞
(他走了。)

Away went he. (×)

c. here 亦為單一副詞，用法亦相同。

例: Mary comes here.
→ Here comes Mary. (○)
(瑪麗來了。)

Here she comes. (○)
　　　代名詞
(她來了。)

Here comes she. (×)

4. 地方副詞片語在句首時，前面可置 there，或其他相關副詞，用以強調該地方副詞片語。there 可置於地方副詞片語之前或之後。但其他相關副詞只能置於地方副詞片語之前。

a. there:

例: On top of the hill lies a beautiful villa.
　　地方副詞片語
= There on top of the hill lies a
　　　　地方副詞片語
beautiful villa.
= On top of the hill there lies a
　地方副詞片語
beautiful villa.
(山丘頂上有棟漂亮的別墅。)

　On the desk is a book.
　　地方副詞片語
= There on the desk is a book.
= On the desk there is a book.
= There is a book on the desk.
(桌上有本書。)

b. 相關副詞:
例: Deep in the mountains lies a small village.
　相關副詞 地方副詞片語
(深山裡有個小村落。)

Not far (away) from here is a post office.
相關副詞 　　　地方副詞片語
(離這兒不遠有間郵局。)

5. 地方副詞或地方副詞片語所形成的倒裝句的好處:
由於倒裝句的主詞在句尾,之後可接形容詞子句、分詞片語
或介系詞片語,用以修飾主詞,擴大主詞的內容,並可避免
主詞在句首修飾語過多的毛病。

例: 未倒裝時:

A man who held a knife in one hand,
　主詞　　　形容詞子句

looking as if he wanted to kill somebody,
　　　　　　分詞片語

stood there. (劣)
不及物動詞 地方副詞

倒裝之後:

→ There stood a man who held a knife in on hand,
　　　不及物動詞 主詞
looking as if he wanted to kill somebody. (佳)
(有名持刀的人站在那兒，看起來像要殺人的樣子。)

A boy with a dog (which) he found the other day
主詞 介系詞片語　　　　形容詞子句

sat in the corner. (劣)
不及物動詞

→ In the corner sat a boy with a dog he found
　　　　　　不及物動詞 主詞
the other day. (佳)
(角落裡坐著個男孩和他前些天撿到的狗。)

6. 注意下列用 here 或 there 置於句首的句子，主詞為代名
詞，因此不倒裝。

a. There you go again.
(你又來這一套了。)

解說: 某甲見到女生，會流口水。某乙對某甲的行為很了解。
某日，某甲與某乙一塊兒出遊。一位漂亮的女生擦肩
而過，某甲就口水直流，某乙邊用臉盆接某甲的口水，
邊罵道，"There you go again."
看完這一段雄哥瞎編的故事，你一定知道如何使用此用

語了吧？！

b. Here we are.
(到了。)

　　解說：某甲要去見某女生，但膽小如鼠，就請某乙一塊
　　　　　陪他去。兩人乘了一部計程車，到了該女生家門
　　　　　口時，某甲，某乙，以及計程車司機都可說這句
　　　　　話："Here we are!"

c. Here you are. (或 Here you go.)
(拿去吧！)

　　解說：某甲到麥當勞買漢堡。服務小姐叫他稍候片刻。不
　　　　　久，服務小姐就把漢堡遞給某甲，同時說了一句：
　　　　　"Here you go."
　　　　　給任何人所要的東西時，均可使用這句話。

d. There you are. (或 There it is.)
(在那裡。)

　　解說：某甲要到叔叔家去，由於是第一次拜訪，在社區裡
　　　　　找了老半天，仍然找不到叔叔家門，幸好雄哥剛好
　　　　　路過，見狀即帶路。指著不遠處一扇鋼門(不好聽，
　　　　　應說成鋼製的門)說道："There you are." 或 "There
　　　　　it is." 某甲連聲道謝後，就飛奔而去。

第四節　完全倒裝句

1. 此類倒裝句係由下列句型演變而成：
   主詞 + be 動詞 + 形容詞(含做形容詞的過去分詞或現在分詞)
   → 形容詞 + be 動詞 + 主詞

   例：$\begin{vmatrix} He \\ One \end{vmatrix}$ who is content $\underline{is}$ $\underline{happy}$.
   $\qquad\qquad\qquad\qquad\qquad$ be adj.
   　　主詞
   → Happy is $\begin{vmatrix} he \\ one \end{vmatrix}$ who is content.

   (知足者常樂。——凡是滿足的人都是快樂的。)

   = $\begin{vmatrix} The\ humble \\ Humble\ people \end{vmatrix}$ $\underline{are}$ $\underline{blessed}$.
   $\qquad\qquad\qquad\qquad$ be　　adj.
   　　　　主
   → $\underline{Blessed}$ $\underline{are}$ $\underline{the\ humble}$.
   (謙虛的人有福了。——凡是謙虛的人都會受到恩寵。)

2. 此類完全倒裝句的主詞，通常泛指所有的人或物。故主詞有
   『凡是……的人或物』之意時，均可使用本倒裝句。

   例：$\underline{A\ man}$ who often helps others $\underline{is}$ $\underline{praiseworthy}$.
   　　主　　　　　　　　　　　　　be　　　adj.
   → $\underline{Praiseworthy}$ $\underline{is}$ a man who often helps others.
   (常助人的人值得讚揚。)

   但有過多修飾語的主詞亦可採用本倒裝句。

   例：$\underline{Noteworthy}$ $\underline{is}$ $\underline{the\ fact}$ that he is talented for music.
   　　adj.　　be　　主詞　名詞子句，做 the fact 的同位語
   (值得一提的是他有音樂的天份。)

第五節　as取代though的倒裝法

1 ．though 所引導的副詞子句屬於下列四種句構時，though 可
　　被 as 取代。

　　a. though ＋ 主詞 ＋ be 動詞 ＋ 形容詞
　　　形容詞可移至句首，再以 as 取代 though。

　　例：| Though | he is nice, I dislike him.
　　　　| Although | 主 be adj.
　　　→ Nice as he is, I dislike him.
　　　→ Nice though he is, I dislike him.
　　　（雖然他很好，我還是不喜歡他。）

　　　但不可譯成：Nice although he is, I dislike him.

　　b. though ＋ 主詞 ＋ be 動詞 ＋ 名詞
　　　名詞可移至句首，再以 as 取代 though。但名詞若爲單
　　　數可數名詞，移至句首時，原有的不定冠詞 a 或 an 一
　　　定要省略。

　　例：| Though | he is a nice boy, I dislike him.
　　　　| Although | 主 be   n.
　　　→ Nice boy | as | he is, I dislike him.
　　　　　　　　　| though |
　　　　A nice boy | as | he is , I dislike him. (×)
　　　　　　　　　　| though |
　　　（雖然他是個好孩子，我還是不喜歡他。）

　　　　| Though | they are nice boys, I dislike them.
　　　　| Although | 主   be   n.
　　　→ Nice boys | as | they are, I dislike them.
　　　　　　　　　 | though |

（雖然他們是好孩子，我還是不喜歡他們。）

c. though 子句中有副詞時，可逕將副詞移至句首，再以 as 取代 though 即成。

例： Though he studied <u>hard</u>, he failed to pass the
　　　　　　　　　　adv.

exam.

→ <u>Hard</u> | as　　　| he studied, he failed to pass the
　　　　　 | though |

exam.

（雖然他努力讀書，還是未能通過考試。）

Though she sings <u>well</u>, she can't dance.
　　　　　　　　　　　adv.

→ <u>Well</u> | as　　　| she sings, she can't dance.
　　　　　 | though |

（她雖然歌唱得好，卻不會跳舞。）

d. though 子句若無副詞時，可在句首添一副詞 much(很)，
再以 as 取代 though 即可。

例： Though <u>he loves me</u>, I dislike him.
　　　　　 無副詞

→ <u>Much</u> | as　　　| he loves me, I dislike him.
　　　　　 | though |

（他雖愛我，我就是不喜歡他。）

Though <u>he wanted to see her</u>, he didn't have
　　　　　　無副詞

the courage.

→ <u>Much</u> | as　　　| he wanted to see her, he didn't
　　　　　 | though |

have the courage.

（他雖然很想見她，卻没有勇氣。）

2．as 若置於句首，則表示『因為』之意，是為副詞連接詞，等於 because。

例： <u>As</u> he is nice, I like him.
　= <u>Because</u> he is nice, I like him.
　（因為他人好，所以我喜歡他。）

但： as 引導的子句，若為主詞 + 一般動詞的句構，且為肯定句時，有下列變化：

<u>As</u> he <u>lives</u> here, he may have ample chances to
　　　　　一般動詞
view the beautiful scenery.
→ <u>Living here as he does</u>, he may...
　（由於他住在這裡，因此會有很多機會欣賞美麗的景色。）

其步驟為：

第一步： 將 as 句中的動詞移至句首，變成現在分詞；

第二步： 再於主詞之後按人稱與時態的不同添加助動詞 do, does 或 did。

例： As he <u>works</u> hard, he is sure to succeed.
　　　　　一般動詞

（一）： 將 works 移至句首，改為現在分詞 working；

（二）： 由於 works 是第三人稱單數現在式動詞，故主詞之後，應加 does。

即成： Working hard as he does, he is sure to succeed.
　　　（由於他努力，因此一定會成功。）

　＊ 唯此類變化較少見，通常不被使用，此處提出來僅供同學參考，不必模仿。

3. 在肯定句中，句構若爲主詞 + 一般動詞，且有副詞 well 修飾時，可將 well 置於句首，再按動詞時態及人稱變化添加助動詞 do, does 或 did，再接主詞，之後置原形動詞。

例: He <u>knows</u> the question <u>well</u>.
　　　 一般動詞
→ <u>Well</u> <u>does</u> he <u>know</u> the question.
　 (他對此問題知之甚詳。)

唯此類用法亦少見，此處提出僅供參考。

Exercise

I. 請選出一個正確的答案:

1. On the other side of the fence _____.
   (A) a man stood with black hair
   (B) had a man with black hair
   (C) stood a man with black hair
   (D) were a man with black hair

2. Under this roof _____ gathered today the most distinguished names of the country.
   (A) are　　(B) be　　(C) is　　(D) being

3. Only when a foreigner has read much English poetry _____ Shakespeare.
   (A) he can understand　　(B) can he understand
   (C) can he understood　　(D) can we understand

4. Nowhere _____ to be found.
   (A) can the missing book　(B) is the missing book
   (C) the missing book is　(D) the missing book can

5. At the gate _____.
   (A) waiting the beggar　(B) waited the beggar
   (C) the beggar waiting　(D) did the beggar wait

6. Only when we give happiness to others regardless of reward _____ we achieve happiness ourselves.
   (A) as　　(B) may　　(C) so　　(D) that

7. She didn't come yesterday, _____ come tomorrow.
   (A) nor she will　　(B) nor she does
   (C) nor will she　　(D) nor does she

8. _____ satisfied with what he had.
   (A) Never had he   (B) Never he was
   (C) Never he had   (D) Never was he

9. An order was given, and _____.
   (A) away they dashed   (B) away dashed they
   (C) dashed they away   (D) away dashed them

10. Only after Norman acquired considerable facility in speaking _____.
    (A) did he learn to read and write
    (B) finally comes reading and writing
    (C) then he learned reading and writing
    (D) he learned to read and write

11. Hardly had she seen her husband _____ she ran to him.
    (A) when   (B) than   (C) as   (D) that

12. Not for a moment _____ the truth of your story.
    (A) he has doubted   (B) he doubts
    (C) did he doubt   (D) he did doubt

13. _____ succeed in doing anything.
    (A) Only by working hard we can
    (B) By only working hard we can
    (C) Only by working hard can we
    (D) Only we can by working hard

14. Not only _____ a promise, but he also kept it.
    (A) did he made   (B) he made
    (C) did he make   (D) he makes

15. Nowhere in the world _____.
    (A) travelers can buy so much beauty for so little money as in Hawaii
    (B) no one can buy so much beauty for so little money

as Hawaii

(C) so much beauty can be bought for so little money in Hawaii

(D) can travelers buy so much beauty for so little money as in Hawaii

16. Never before in similar circumstances _____.

(A) a British Prime Minister had refused to step down

(B) did a British Prime Minister have refused to step down

(C) a British Prime Minister have refused to step down

(D) had a British Prime Minister refused to step down

17. _____ received law degrees as today.

(A) Never so many women have

(B) Never have so many women

(C) The women aren't ever

(D) Women who have never

18. Flying demands a much greater supply of energy _____ other forms of transportation.

(A) than do most　　　　(B) most than do

(C) than most do　　　　(D) do than most

19. On the right _____.

(A) Mr. Fleming saw the foremost lines of the students

(B) saw Mr. Fleming the foremost lines of the students

(C) were seen by Mr. Fleming the foremost lines of the students

(D) the foremost lines of the students were seen by Mr. Fleming

20. Not far from the upper ford _____.

(A) they met an old friend of theirs

(B) met they an old friend of theirs

(C) was met by them an old friend of theirs

(D) there was met an old friend of theirs by them.

2 1 . "Have you ever been to Europe before, Martha?" "_____."
(A) Never I have been there before
(B) Never did I been there before
(C) Never have I been there before
(D) I have been never there before

2 2 . "Is Conrad always on time, Pierre?" "_____."
(A) Seldom does he come on time
(B) Seldom is he on time
(C) Seldom he is on time
(D) He seldom come on time

2 3 . "Can you understand what the old man says, Harry?"
"_____."
(A) Hardly can I understand what does he say
(B) I can hardly understand what does he say
(C) Can I hardly understand what he says
(D) Hardly can I understand what he says

2 4 . "Did you see Liza make any mistake, Nancy?" "_____."
(A) Rarely have I seen her make any mistake
(B) Rarely I have seen her make any mistake
(C) Rarely have seen I her make any mistake
(D) I have seen her making any mistake rarely

2 5 . "Does Lewis come here to see you very often, Nina?"
"_____."
(A) Scarcely does he come here to see us
(B) Scarcely has he come here to see us
(C) He scarcely come here to see us
(D) Scarcely is he come to see us

2 6 . One of the walls of his room was lined with cupboards
and bookcases; on the other _____.

(A) hung pictures of men and places
(B) pictures of men and places hanged there
(C) he hanged many pictures of men and places
(D) was hung pictures of men and places

2 7 . Close behind the entrenchment _____.
(A) they came upon dozens of soldiers
(B) came they upon dozens of soldiers
(C) dozens of soldiers were come upon by them
(D) they had came upon dozens of soldiers.

2 8 . On the northwest side of the island _____.
(A) have signs of the incessant influence of the wind and sea
(B) there have signs of the incessant influence of the wind and sea
(C) are signs of the incessant influence of the wind and sea
(D) is signs of the incessant influence of the wind and sea

2 9 . With the cultural boom _____.
(A) a boom in education has come along with it
(B) has came a boom in education with it
(C) has come a boom in education
(D) there has a boom in education

3 0 . Meg opened the box. Inside _____.
(A) a diamond ring was there
(B) a diamond ring lies there
(C) was a diamond ring
(D) a diamond ring was found

標準答案: 1.(C)　2.(A)　3.(B)　4.(B)　5.(B)　6.(B)　7.(C)
8.(D)　9.(A) 10.(A) 11.(A) 12.(C) 13.(C) 14.(C)
15.(D) 16.(D) 17.(B) 18.(A) 19.(A) 20.(A) 21.(C)

22.(B) 23.(D) 24.(A) 25.(A) 26.(A) 27.(A) 28.(C)
29.(C) 30.(C)

習題解答：

1. 主詞 + 不及物動詞 + 介詞片語
 → 介詞片語 + 不及物動詞 + 主詞

2. 主詞 + be + P.P. + 介詞片詞
 → 介詞片語 + be + P.P. + 主詞

3. only when（唯有當……）引導的副詞子句置於句首時，該主
 要子句須倒裝。

4. 否定副詞置於句首，該句須倒裝。

5. 與第一題同理。

6. 與第三題同理。

7. ..., nor will she come tomorrow.
 = ..., and neither will she come tomorrow.
 = ..., and she will not come tomorrow, either.

8. 與第四題同理。

9. 地方副詞置於句首時，若該主詞為代名詞，則主詞與動詞不可
 倒裝。

10. 與第三題同理。

11. 主詞 + had hardly + P.P. + when + 過去式子句
 = Hardly had + 主詞 + P.P. + when + 過去式子句
 一……就……

12. 否定副詞片語置於句首時，該句須倒裝。

１３．與上題同理。

１４．與上題同理。

１５．與上題同理。

１６．否定副詞置於句首，該句須倒裝。

１７．與十六題同理。

１８．...than most other...do
　 = ...than do most other...
　　此處的 do 原應置於句尾，但因主詞過長，故與之倒裝。

１９．介詞片語置於句首時，若該句動詞爲及物動詞，則不可與主詞
　　倒裝。

２０．本句中的主詞 they 爲代名詞，動詞 met 爲及物動詞，故該
　　句雖有地方副詞片語置於句首亦無須倒裝。

２１．否定副詞置於句首，該句須倒裝。

２２．與二十一題同理。

２３．與二十一題同理。

２４．與二十一題同理。

２５．與二十一題同理。

２６．...; on the other wall hung pictures of men and places.
　 =...; on the other hung pictures of men and places.
　　本句因介詞片語置於句首，動詞 hung 爲不及物動詞，故形成
　　倒裝。原句中的 wall 因與前面重覆，故予以省略。

２７．與第九題同理。

28. 與第一題同理。

29. 與第一題同理。

30. 地方副詞置於句首時，主詞必須與不及物動詞倒裝。

第十章
比較句構

概說:

約三十年前，雄哥在中學階段唸英文的時候，不是個很用功的學生。當時喜歡穿喇叭褲，不時將高中大盤帽的兩側往內擠壓，看起來像個希特勒式的軍帽。有事沒事，嘴裡咬嚼著一片口香糖，輕哼著西洋歌曲，自認洋派得很。旁人總以為雄哥的英文好得很，但雄哥心裡有數，因為在班上的英語成績排名總是最後幾名。

有一天，英文老師正巧教授比較句構的形成及用法，雄哥沒專心聽(因為覺得太過複雜)，就被老師狠揍了一頓(當時是可以體罰的)。雄哥個性硬，心一橫，就誓言不再聽英文課了。而從此以後，雄哥的英文成績也就變成了個位數。

現在雄哥寫比較句構時，心中真有無限的感慨，三十年後的今天，比較句構對雄哥而言實在易如反掌。但雄哥畢竟走了好長的一段學習路程。為使同學在短短幾天內學得雄哥的累積經驗，雄哥執筆本章時，儘量以簡潔易懂的筆調撰寫。只要有耐心，你一定會弄懂比較句構的。在看本章之前，請同學先看下列的句子，即使不懂亦沒關係。

比較句構要靠兩種副詞連接詞形成：than, as。
基本句型有兩種：

1. 原級比較：**as**

   例: He is <u>as</u> <u>diligent</u> <u>as</u> Peter.
   　　　　副詞　　　　副詞連接詞
   (他和彼得一樣用功。)

   　　He doesn't study <u>so</u> hard <u>as</u> Peter.
   　　　　　　　　　　　副詞　　　副詞連接詞
   (他沒有彼得用功。)

2．一般比較：than

　例：He is <u>more</u> diligent <u>than</u> Peter.
　　　　　副詞　　　　　副詞連接詞
　　（他比彼得用功。）

　　　He doesn't study <u>harder</u> <u>than</u> Peter.
　　　　　　　　　　　副詞　　副詞連接詞
　　（他沒有比彼得用功。）

第一節　一般比較句構

1．一般比較句構，一定要使用副詞連接詞 than。
　造句方式：

　a．先造一個含有形容詞或副詞的句子；
　　例：He is <u>prudent</u>.
　　　　　　　　adj.
　　　（他很小心。）

　　　　He runs <u>fast</u>.
　　　　　　　　adv.
　　　（他跑得快。）

　b．再將句中形容詞或副詞變成比較級，即 | more | + | adj. | ；
　　　　　　　　　　　　　　　　　　　| less |　| adv. |
　　例：He is <u>more</u> prudent.
　　　（他比較小心。）

　　　　He runs <u>less</u> fast.
　　　（他跑得比較不快。）

　c．再設定比較對象，並在該比較對象之前置副詞連接詞 than，即告完成。

例: He is <u>more</u> prudent <u>than</u> Peter.
　　　　　　　　　　　　　　　　比較對象

（他比彼得小心。）

　　　　He runs <u>less</u> fast <u>than</u> Peter.
　　　　　　　　　　　　　　　　比較對象

（他跑得沒有彼得快。）

2. 理論基礎：
　　than 之後原本並非單一的比較對象，而是與主要子句句構完全相同的副詞子句。該副詞子句修飾主要子句中的比較副詞 more 或 less。

　　即: <u>He</u> <u>is</u> <u>more</u> prudent <u>than</u> <u>Peter</u> <u>is</u> prudent.
　　　　S　be　比副　adj.　副連　S　be　adj.
　　　　　　　　　　↑　　　　　　副詞子句

　　　　<u>He</u> <u>runs</u> <u>less</u> fast <u>than</u> <u>Peter</u> <u>runs</u> <u>fast</u>.
　　　　S　vi.　比副　adv.　副連　S　vi.　adv.
　　　　　　　　　↑　　　　　　副詞子句

　　但: 為了避免重複，than 子句僅保留比較對象，相同的述詞部份（即動詞及動詞以後的字）均予省略，而形成：
　　　　He is more prudent than Peter.

　　　　He runs less fast than Peter.

3. than 副詞子句句構中，若有 be 動詞可將之保留；若有助動詞（can, will, shall, have, has,...等）亦可保留；若有一般動詞，則應以 do, does, did 代替。當然這些 be 動詞、助動詞或 do, does, did 可以省略，亦可倒裝。

　　a. be 動詞
　　　例: He is less responsible | than you (are).
　　　　　　　　　　　　　　　　　　　| than are you.

（他沒有你負責任。）

b. 助動詞
例: He can sing more beautifully │ than you (can).
│ than can you.

（他唱得比你悅耳。）

c. 一般動詞
例: He worked more carefully │ than you (did).
│ than did you.

（他工作比你要小心。）

4. 絕大多數的副詞或形容詞（特別是三音節以上的副詞或形容詞），被 more 修飾時，均保留原級形態，但單音節或某些兩音節的副詞或形容詞則是不規則變化，無須被 more 修飾。

例: 三音節: She is more beautiful than Mary.
（她比瑪莉漂亮。）

兩音節: He is more prudent than Peter.
（他比彼得小心。）

但: 兩音節: He is more clever than Peter. (×)
→ He is cleverer than Peter. (○)
（他比彼得聰明。）

單音節: He runs more fast than Peter. (×)
→ He runs faster than Peter. (○)

注意:
有些字變成比較級時，甚至連原來的樣子都改變了。

例: He speaks English well.
→ He speaks English better (非 more well) than John.
（他英文說得比約翰好。）

He is bad.

→ He is worse (非 more bad) than John.
（他比約翰壞。）

因此，副詞或形容詞形成比較級時，我們應注意其是否為規則變化或不規則變化，一般字典中或普通的參考書均有列出來。由於這些詞類變化非技術性的東西，雄哥不打算列出來，亂湊篇幅，浪費本文法書的寶貴空間。相信同學肯查字典，多看文章，自己就會了解的。（雄哥就是這樣學英文的。）

5. less 之後的副詞或形容詞，不論任何音節，均使用原級。

例: He is less good than John. (○)
（他沒有約翰好。）
He is less better than John. (×)

He speaks English less well than John. (○)
（他英文說得沒有約翰好。）
He speaks English less better than John. (×)

He does things less carefully than John. (○)
（他做事沒有約翰小心。）

6. 比較句中通常比較對象是不同的人或物，但亦有與自己做比較的情形發生。

例: He studies harder than he did. (= studied hard)
　　　　　　自己比較
（他比從前用功。）

She looks younger than she is (young).
（她看起來比實際年輕。）

注意:

a. 自行做比較時，句中的時態若不同，即主要子句爲現在式，than 子句爲過去式，則 than 之後的主詞以及其後之過去式 be 動詞、助動詞或一般動詞變成的 did 不可省略。

(1) be 動詞

例: He is healthier than he was.
　　　└─不同時態─────┘
　　(他比以前健康。)

(2) 助動詞

例: He can sing better than he could.
　　　└──不同時態──────┘
　　(他比從前唱得好。)

(3) 一般動詞

例: He works harder than he did.
　　　└─不同時態───────(= worked hard)
　　= He works harder than he used to (work hard).
　　(他工作比從前努力。)

b. 此類不同時態的自行比較句構中，主要子句及 than 子句均有對等的介系詞片語，或 than 子句有另一 when 引導的副詞子句修飾時，than 之後的主詞及動詞或助動詞部份可以省略。

(1) 介系詞片語

例: He is happier with Mary than he is (happy) with
　　　　　　　　　　　↑　　　　　　　　　　　↑
　　Jane.　　　└────對等介詞片語────┘
　　= He is happier with Mary than with Jane.
　　(他和瑪莉在一起比和珍妮在一起快樂。)

He is more interested in English than he is
　　　　　　　　　　　　　↓　　　↑
(interested) in Japanese. 對等介詞片語

```
= He is more interested in English than in
  Japanese.
```
（他對英文比對日文有興趣。）

注意:
介系詞片語對稱時，第二個片語中的介系詞千萬不可省略，
否則會造成對象的錯誤比較。

例:
```
He is more interested in English than he is in
Japanese. (○)
He is more interested in English than
Japanese. (×)
```
```
= Japanese is interested in English. (×)
```
（他對英文的興趣比日文對英文的興趣高。）

不過有時候我們亦會在一段文章中見到這種錯誤的比較，
勉強可以接受，但對嚴謹學習文法的我們應予以避免。

(2) when 子句

例:
```
He is much older than (he was) when I saw
him ten years ago.
```
副詞子句
```
→ He is much older than when I saw him ten
  years ago.
```
（他比我十年前看見他時老多了。）

```
He is much older than I saw him ten years
ago. (×) 比較對象錯誤
```

理由:
本句成了 He 與 I 在做比較，而非 He 與 he 做比較。

7. 比較句構中，若主要子句為『主詞 + 及物動詞 + 受詞』，而
than 子句亦為『主詞 + 及物動詞 + 受詞』，且兩個及物動詞
均相同時，than 子句的動詞可用 do, does, did 取代。

例: I love you more than he loves you.
　　　↑——相同動詞————↑

= I love you more than he does you.
（我比他愛你。）

　I love you more than I love Mary.
　　　↑———相同動詞————↑

= I love you more than I do Mary.
（我愛你比愛瑪莉多。）

　千萬不要造這樣的句子:

I love you more than Mary.

理由:
本句可能有兩個意思:

a. I love you more than Mary loves you.
（我比瑪莉愛你。）

b. I love you more than I love Mary.
（我愛你比愛瑪莉多。）

　因此，語意不詳，故應改爲

I love you more than Mary does. (does 不宜省略)
（我比瑪莉愛你。）

或 I love you more than I do Mary.
（我愛你比愛瑪莉多。）

8. 數量形容詞 much, little, many, few 變成比較級時，有下列變化:
a. much（很多的），little（很少的）修飾不可數名詞:

原級　　　比較級　　　最高級

```
much        more        the most
little      less        the least
```

例：原級：He has much money.
　　　　（他有很多錢。）

　比較級：He has more money than John (does).
　　　　　（他比約翰有錢。）

　最高級：He has the most money of all.
　　　　　（他是所有人中最有錢的。）

　　原級：He has little time.
　　　　　（他的時間很少。）

　比較級：He has less time than I (do) for the job.
　　　　　（他做這工作用的時間比我少。）

　最高級：He has the least time of all.
　　　　　（他用的時間最少。）

b. many（很多的），few（很少的）修飾可數的複數名詞：

例：原級：He has many friends.
　　　　（他有很多朋友。）

　比較級：He has more friends than John.
　　　　　（他的朋友比約翰多。）

　最高級：He has the most friends of all.
　　　　　（他的朋友最多。）

　　原級：He has few friends.
　　　　　（他朋友很少。）

　比較級：He has fewer friends than John.

（他的朋友比約翰少。）

最高級：He has the fewest friends of all.
（他的朋友最少。）

9.『主詞 + 介詞片語』或『所有格 + 主詞』極易形成對象的錯誤比較，應予避免。

例：People in Taiwan lead a much better life than
　　主詞　　介詞片語
mainland China. (×)

理由：
people 是人，mainland China 是地方，故形成對象的錯誤比較。

改正：
People in Taiwan lead a much better life than
　　主詞　　介詞片語
those in mainland China. (○)
主詞　　　　介詞片語
（台灣人民比大陸人民生活富足。）

His car is better than his friends. (×)
所有格 主詞

理由：
car 為物，his friends 為人，比較對象錯誤。

改正：
His car is better than | his friends'.
所有格 主詞　　　　　 | those of his friends.
（他的車子比他朋友們的好。）

注意：
使用 that 或 those 做代名詞時，that 代替單數的名詞（或不可數名詞)，those 則代替複數的名詞。

例: I have found that John's <u>interest</u> in English
　　　　　　　　　　　　　　　單數 n.
is greater than <u>that</u> of his classmate Peter.
(我發現約翰對英文的興趣要比他同學彼得高。)

The <u>stamps</u> he has collected are more exotic than
複數 n.
<u>those</u> Peter has collected.
(他收集的郵票比彼得收集的要奇特。)

10. 有些形容詞 (包括由其演變過來的副詞)，本身就有『至極』
或『最高級』的意味，不能使用在比較級句構中。這些字常
用的有: perfect (完美的), sublime (卓越的), noble (
高貴的), extreme (極度的), superb (極好的), excellent
(極好的)等。

例: He speaks English <u>more perfectly</u> than John. (×)
理由:
perfectly 即已表『完美無缺』，故無比較級。

11. 某些 -ior 結尾的形容詞本身已具有比較級的味道，不可用
more...than 或 less...than 修飾，而要與介系詞 to 並
用。
常用的此類形容詞一共有四個:

superior to 　　　比……優越的
inferior to 　　　比……差勁的
senior to 　　　　比……年長的；
　　　　　　　　　比……地位高的
junior to 　　　　比……年輕的；
　　　　　　　　　比……地位低的

例: I really doubt John's competence; it seems quite
obvious that he is inferior to his friend David.

（我眞懷疑約翰的能力，很明顯地，他比他朋友大衛差
勁。）

Even though he is <u>superior to</u> most of his classmates, he is not arrogant.
（雖然他比其他同學優秀，卻不會高傲。）

I am <u>senior to</u> <u>him</u> by five years.
                      O.
= I am five years his <u>senior</u>.
                            n.
= I am older than <u>he</u> by five years.
                   S
（我比他年長五歲。）

Mary is <u>senior to</u> her husband in the company,
but back home she is <u>junior to</u> him.
（在公司裡，瑪莉的職位比先生高，但回到家裡，她的地位
便在其夫之下。）

其他類似的詞類：

prior to + n.　　在……之前(指時間)
= before + n.

posterior to + n.　在……之後(指時間)
= after + n.

例: <u>Prior to</u> the war, he was a teacher.
（在戰前，他是名老師。）

<u>Posterior to</u> the war, he left the army.
（在戰後，他離開了軍隊。）

12. 注意同範圍及不同範圍的比較：

a. 同範圍:
　某人或某物屬於同一團體或種類，寫作者欲將之與該團體或種類的其他所有份子做比較時，採下列句型，以避免將該人或該物形成重疊比較:

人: John is better than | any other student
　　　　　　　　　　　　| all (the) other students
　　　　　　　　　　　　| all (the) others
　　　　　　　　　　　　| anyone else

　　in his class.
　　同範圍
　　(約翰比班上其他學生優秀。)

物: Taipei is bigger than | any other city
　　　　　　　　　　　　　| all (the) other cities

　　in Taiwan.
　　同範圍
　　(台北比台灣其他的都市要大。)

b. 不同範圍:
　寫作者欲將某人或某物與不同的**團體或種類**的所有份子做比較時，any 或 all 之後無須加 other 一字。句型如下:

人: John is better than | any student
　　　　　　　　　　　　| all (the) students
　　　　　　　　　　　　| anyone
　　　　　　　　　　　　　　代
　　　　　　　　　　　　| all
　　　　　　　　　　　　　代

　　in Mary's class.
　　不同範圍
　　(約翰比瑪莉班上所有的同學優秀。)

物: Taipei is bigger than | any city
　　　　　　　　　　　　　| all (the) cities

　　in Nepal.

（台北比尼泊爾任何城市都要來得大。）

13. be getting more and more + adj.　愈來愈……的
  = be getting increasingly + adj.

例: Life over there is getting
  | more and more difficult.
  | adj.
  | increasingly difficult.
  (那兒的生活越來越不容易。)

His English is getting more and more good. (×)
                                       adj.

理由:
good 的比較級形態應爲 better，無 more good
的用法。
改正:
His English is getting | better and better.
                       | increasingly good.
(他的英文越來越好。)

注意:
increasingly 等於 more and more，之後不必再接比較
級。

例: His English is getting increasingly
  | better. (劣)
  | good. (佳)

The weather is getting | hotter and hotter.
                       | increasingly hot.
(天氣愈來愈熱。)

14. 修飾比較級的副詞或形容詞通常有六個副詞，置於被修飾的副
   詞或形容詞之前:

much, far, a lot, a great deal, a lot, still, even。

例: This question is | far | more
　　　　　　　　　　| much
　　　　　　　　　　| a lot
　　　　　　　　　　| a great deal
　　　　　　　　　　| still
　　　　　　　　　　| even

difficult than that one.
(這問題比那個要難多了。)

He studies much harder than anyone of them.
(他比他們之中任何一個都用功得多。)

注意:

a. 這六個副詞亦可修飾 superior, inferior, senior, junior。

例: This car is | far | superior to that
　　　　　　　 | much
　　　　　　　 | a lot
　　　　　　　 | a great deal
　　　　　　　 | still
　　　　　　　 | even

one.
(這輛車比那輛好得太多了。)

b. 這六個副詞亦可修飾副詞 too。

例: He is | much | too old to do the work.
　　　　　| far
　　　　　| a lot
　　　　　| a great deal
　　　　　| still
　　　　　| even

(他太老了，無法做這差事。)

15. 最高級副詞
    最高級副詞有兩個 most 及 least 可用以修飾句中的形容詞、
    副詞或動詞。

    a. 形容詞

        例: She is the most beautiful girl (that) I've
                     └────↑adj.

            ever seen.
            (她是我見過最美的女孩。)

            Of the three girls, she is the least beautiful.
                                            └────↑adj.

            (三個女孩之中，她最不好看。)

    b. 副詞

        例: He treats people most politely.
                            └────↑adv.

            (他對人極為有禮。)

    c. 動詞

        例: I need you most.
              vt.└────┘
            (我最需要你。)

            I least expected to see you here.
              └────↑vt.
            (我最不希望在這裡見到你。)

    注意:
    某些副詞或形容詞由於不規則變化的關係，變成最高級時，並
    不需要 most 或 least 修飾，即可自成最高級的副詞或形容
    詞。

原級		比較級	最高級
good (adj.)	好的	better	best
hot (adj.)	熱的	hotter	hottest
bad (adj.)	壞的	worse	worst
hard (adv.)	努力地	harder	hardest
(adj.)	硬的；難的	harder	hardest

雄哥不打算一一列出來，以免佔篇幅。這些字同學在平常閱讀文章查字典均可看得到。

例: She is the best student of all.
（她是全部學生中最好的一個。）

　Of the five students here, she studies hardest.
（在這五個學生中，她最用功。）

16. 使用最高級副詞或形容詞所形成的比較對象一定是三者以上，通常出現在下列兩個句構中：

a. of｜the three｜...　　在｜這三個……｜之中
　(among)｜the four｜　　　｜這四個｜
　　　　　｜　　:　｜　　　　｜　　:　｜
　　　　　｜　　:　｜　　　　｜　　:　｜
　　　　　｜all　｜　　　　｜所有｜

例: Of the five books, I like that one best.
　　　　　　　　　　　　vt.↑————————adv.
（五本書中，我最喜歡那本。）

He is the best student of all.
　　　adj.——↑n.
（他是所有學生中最好的一個。）

注意:
of the two 則使用比較級。

例: Of the two students, John is the better.
　　　　　　　　　　　　↑
　　　　　　　　　　　　　　　　　　┘adj.

(這兩個學生中，約翰比較好。)

Of the two books, I like that one better.
　　　　　　　　　　　　↑
　　　　　　　　　　　　　　　　　　─adv.

(這兩本書中，我比較喜歡那本。)

b. 最高級形容詞 + n. + 關係代名詞 that (不可使用 who,
whom, which) + 完成式形容詞子句

例: John is the most responsible man (that) I've
　　　　　　最高級 adj.
ever known.
完成式形容詞子句
(約翰是我所認識最有責任感的人。)

He is the best student (that) I've ever taught.
　　　最高級 adj.　　　　　　完成式形容詞子句
(他是我教過最好的學生。)

That's the greatest idea that has ever occurred
　　　　最高級 adj.　　　　　完成式形容詞子句
to me.
(那是我所想到過最棒的構想。)

17. 最高級副詞修飾動詞或副詞時，不必加定冠詞 the，但最高級
形容詞修飾名詞時，則須加 the。

a. 副詞

例: Of the four students, he treats people
most　　　　politely.
最高級 adv. adv.↑

the most politely.

（四個學生中，他對人最有禮。）

b. 動詞

例: Of all the people I know, I <u>respect</u> him <u>most</u>.
　　　　　　　　　　　　　　　　vt.　　　　最高級 adv.

<u>the</u> most.

（我所認識的人中，我最敬佩他。）

He <u>studies</u> <u>hardest</u>　　of all.
　　　vi.　　　最高級 adv.

<u>the</u> hardest

（他是所有人中最用功的一個。）

c. 名詞

例: He is <u>the best</u> <u>student</u> of all.
　　　　　最高級 adj. n.

（他是所有學生當中最好的一個。）

I find Mary <u>the most beautiful</u> <u>girl</u> in her
　　　　　　最高級 adj.　　　　n.

class.
（我覺得瑪莉是她班上最美的女孩。）

18. 最高級形容詞修飾名詞時，前面因為加了定冠詞 the，而 the
　　+ adj. 可做代名詞用，故之後的名詞可省略。

例: She is <u>the most beautiful</u> <u>girl</u> of all.
　　　　　　　　adj.　　　　n.
　= She is <u>the most beautiful</u> of all (the girls).
　　　　　　　代名詞

（她是所有女孩中最美的一個。）

　Of all the boys, he is <u>the cleverest</u> (boy).
（所有男孩中，他最聰明。）

１９．最高級的句構可被下列句構取代：

例：He is <u>the best</u> student of all.
= | No one else is | is | better than | he.
　| No (other) student | | as good as |
　| | | so good as |
（他是所有學生中最好的一個。）

　He studies <u>hardest</u> of all.
= No one (else) studies | harder than | he.
　| as hard as |
　| so hard as |
（他是所有人中最用功的一個。）

２０．most 亦可做 very（很）解，加形容詞修飾名詞時，不必於 most 之前加定冠詞。

例：She is really a | most | beautiful girl.
　| very |
（她是個很美的女孩子。）

２１．帶有 the 的最高級的副詞或形容詞，可被 by far 及 much 兩個副詞修飾。

例：She is | by far | <u>the most</u> beautiful girl in town.
　| much |
（她是鎮上最美的女孩子。）

　I find him | by far | <u>the best</u> student of all.
　| much |
（我發覺他是所有學生中最棒的一個。）

第二節

原級比較句構

1. 原級比較句構出現在含有『as...as』(和……一樣地) 的句構中。

造句方式:

a. 先造一個含有形容詞或副詞的句子;
例: He is prudent.
　　　　　adj.
(他很小心。)

He runs fast.
　　　　adv.
(他跑得快。)

b. 再於句中的形容詞或副詞之前置 as 一字;
as 爲副詞, 譯成『一樣地』。
例: He is as prudent.
　　　　adv. adj.

(他一樣地小心。)

He runs as　　fast.
　　　　adv. adv.

(他跑得一樣快。)

c. 再設定比較對象, 並在該比較對象之前置副詞連接詞 as,
即告完成。此 as 譯成『和』。
例: He is as prudent as John.
　　　　一樣地　　　　和

（他和約翰一樣小心。）

He runs <u>as</u> fast <u>as</u> John.
　　　 一樣地　　　和
（他跑得和約翰一樣快。）

2．理論基礎：
上例句中，第二個 as 為副詞連接詞，之後本應有一個與主要子句完全一樣的句構，是副詞子句，修飾第一個 as (adv. 一樣地)。
即：<u>He</u> <u>is</u> <u>as</u>　<u>prudent</u> <u>as</u>　<u>John</u> <u>is</u> <u>prudent</u>.
　　 S　be　adv. adj.　 副連　 S　be adj.
　　　　 （一樣地）　 （和）
　　　　　　　　　　　　　　　副詞子句

<u>He</u> <u>runs</u> <u>as</u>　<u>fast</u> <u>as</u>　<u>John</u> <u>runs</u> <u>fast</u>.
 S　vi.　adv. adv. 副連　 S　 vi. adv.
　　　 （一樣地）（和）
　　　　　　　　　　副詞子句

但為了避免重複，as 子句僅保留比較對象，相同的述詞部份（即動詞及動詞以後的字）均予省略，而形成：

He is as prudent as John.

He runs as fast as John.

3．一如 than 子句，as 子句的變化如下：

a. be 動詞
　例：He is <u>as</u> prudent │ as John (is).
　　　　　　　　　　　　 │ as <u>is</u> <u>John</u>.
　（他和約翰一樣小心。）

b. 助動詞

例: He can sing as well | as John (can).
　　　　　　　　　　　 | as can John.
（他唱得和約翰一樣好。）

c. 一般動詞
例: He runs as fast | as John (does).
　　　　　　　　　 | as does John.
（他跑得和約翰一樣快。）

4. as...as 用於肯定句或否定句中，而 so...as 則只用於否定句中。
例:
肯定句: He studies as hard as Mary.
　　　　　（他和瑪莉一樣用功。）

　　　　　He is as thin as a rail.
　　　　　（他和鐵軌一樣瘦——他瘦極了。）

否定句: He doesn't study | as | hard as Mary.
　　　　　　　　　　　　 | so |
　　　　　（他沒有瑪莉用功。）

　　　　　He isn't | as | polite as John.
　　　　　　　　　 | so |
　　　　　（他沒有約翰有禮貌。）

第三節

其他有關 as/than 的重要用法

1. as...as...之中，可插入含有形容詞的單數可數名詞。(見本書上冊第１８５頁。)

造句方法:

a. 先造一個含有形容詞的單數可數名詞的句子;
例: He is a handsome boy.
　　　　　　adj.　　n.

b. 再將第一個 as 置於該名詞之前;
即: He is as a handsome boy. (×)

由於 as 是副詞 (一樣地)，不能修飾不定冠詞 a，故須將形容詞 handsome 與 a 互換位置，使 handsome 緊鄰 as 之後，以供其修飾。
即: He is as handsome a boy.
　　　　　adv.　adj.

c. 再將第二個 as 置於 a boy 之後，然後接比較對象，即告完成。
即: He is as handsome a boy as John.
(他和約翰一樣是英俊的男孩。)

例: I have as good a car as that one.
(我有一輛車和那輛一樣好。)

注意:
(1) 類似此種只能與單數名詞並用的句構尚有:
so...that 如此……以致

```
too...to      太……而不
how...        多麼地……
```

(a) so...that

例: He is so good a boy that I like him very much.

= He is such a good boy that I like him very much.

(他是如此好的男孩，我非常喜歡他。)

(b) too...to

例: He is too old a man to do it.

(他人太老了，没法做此事。)

(c) how

例: How great a man he is!

= What a great man he is!

(他人眞好！)

(2) what 與 such 之後可修飾單複數或不可數名詞。

例: What a great man he is!
　　　　　單數 n.

(他人眞好！)

What beautiful music it is!
　　　　不可數 n.

(眞好聽的音樂！)

What good boys they are!
　　　　複數 n.

(他們眞是好孩子！)

He is such a good boy that I like him.
　　　　　單數 n.

(他是這麼好的孩子，我喜歡他。)

They are such <u>good boys</u> that I like them.
              複數 n.
(他們是這麼好的孩子，我喜歡他們。)

It is such <u>good music</u> that I enjoy it.
             不可數 n.
(這音樂這麼好，我很欣賞。)

2. as...as one can　　盡可能地……
  = as...as possible
　a. 造句方法:

　　(1) 先造一個含有形容詞或副詞的句子;
　　　　例: You must study <u>hard</u>.
　　　　　　　　　　　　　　adv.
　　　　(你一定要用功。)

　　　　He remained <u>quiet</u>.
　　　　　　　　　　　　adj.
　　　　(他保持沈默。)

　　(2) 在 hard 或 quiet 之前置入第一個 as (adv. 一樣地);
　　　　即: You must study <u>as</u> hard.

　　　　He remained <u>as</u> quiet.

　　(3) 句尾添入 as one (you, he...) can 或 possible,
　　　　即告完成。
　　　　即: You must study <u>as</u> hard | as you can.
　　　　　　　　　　　　　　　　　　　| as possible.

　　　　(你要盡可能地用功。)

　　　　He remained <u>as</u> quiet | as he could.
　　　　　　　　　　　　　　　　| as possible.
　　　　(他盡可能地保持安靜。)

　b. 理論基礎:

(1) as one can 之後省略了與前面主要子句中相同的述詞部份，以避免贅敘。

例: You must <u>study</u> as <u>hard</u> as you can <u>study hard</u>.

————重複————

→ You must study as hard <u>as you can</u>.

He <u>remained</u> as <u>quiet</u> as he could <u>remain quiet</u>.

————重複————

→ He remained as quiet <u>as he could</u>.

(2) as possible 係為 as it is (was) possible 化簡而成，it 是代名詞，代替前面相同的述詞部份。

例: You must <u>study</u> as <u>hard</u> as <u>it</u> is possible.

= You must study as hard as <u>studying hard</u> is possible.　　動名詞(做主詞)

He <u>remained</u> as <u>quiet</u> as <u>it</u> was possible.

= He remained as quiet as <u>remaining quiet</u> was possible.　　動名詞(做主詞)

由於 as it is possible 經常使用的關係，已演變成將 it is 省略而形成 as possible 的片語。
即: You must study as hard <u>as possible</u>.

He remained as quiet <u>as possible</u>.

3. as...as any　　與任何人一樣 = 乃是最……

例: He is as happy a man as any.
= He is the happiest man.

(他是最快樂的人。)

4. as...as ever 與往常一樣

例: Though it has been a long time since I parted from
him, he is as young as ever.
(雖然我和他分開已久, 他還是和從前一樣年輕。)

5. as...as ever lived 古今最……
= the 最高級...that ever lived

例: He is as great a hero as ever lived.
= He is the greatest hero that ever lived.
(他是古今最偉大的英雄。)

6. more...than 句構中, 若為兩個形容詞相互比較, 則該兩個
形容詞一律使用原級。

例: He is more good than bad.
adj. adj.
(他好的成份大過壞的成份——與其說他壞, 倒不如說他
好。)
= He is not so bad as good.
= He is good rather than bad.

但: He is more good than John. (×)
→ He is better than John. (○)
(他比約翰好。)

7. 倍數詞造句法

a. 本句構一共有四種:
(1) 倍數詞 + as...as 是……的幾倍

(2) more than + 倍數詞 + as...as
是……的幾倍還不止

(3) 倍數詞 + the (或 所有格) + 名詞
是……的幾倍

(4) more than + 倍數詞 + the (或 所有格) + 名詞
是……的幾倍還不止

例: He is three times as rich as I.
(他的財富是我的三倍。)

He is more than three times as rich as I.
(他的財富是我的三倍還不止。)

He has three times my money.
(他的錢是我的三倍。)

He has more than three times my money.
(他的錢是我的三倍還不止。)

b. 倍數詞 + as...as　　是……的幾倍

本句構因含有 as...as 片語，故句中必須有形容詞或副詞
，才能使用本句構。造句的步驟如下:

譯: 他用功的程度是我的三倍。

第一步: 先譯『他用功。』
He studies hard.
得知有副詞 hard

第二步: 再譯『他和我一樣用功。』
He studies as hard as I.

第三步: 將倍數詞 three times (三倍) 置於 as...as
之前，而完成整句的翻譯。
He studies three times as hard as I.
　　　　　倍數詞　　　 副詞

（他用功的程度是我的三倍。）

注意:
上句以副詞 hard 為依據，而完成倍數詞的句構。我們亦
可採形容詞 diligent （用功的，勤勉的）譯出意思相同的
句子:

第一步: 先譯『他用功。』
　　　　He is diligent.
　　　　得知有形容詞 diligent

第二步: 再譯『他和我一樣用功。』
　　　　He is <u>as</u> diligent <u>as</u> I.

第三步: 將倍數詞 three times 置於 as...as 之前，而
　　　　完成整句的翻譯。
　　　　He is <u>three times</u> <u>as</u> <u>diligent</u> <u>as</u> I.
　　　　　　 倍數詞 　　　　　　形容詞
　　　　（他比我用功三倍。）

由此得知，只要有副詞或形容詞，就可使用本句構。

譯: 我的年紀是他的三倍。

第一步: I am old.
第二步: I am <u>as</u> old <u>as</u> he.
第三步: I am <u>three times</u> <u>as</u> old <u>as</u> he.

c. more than + 倍數詞 + as...as　　　是……的幾倍還不止

本句構與 b. 中的句構大致一樣，只是在倍數詞之前加了
more than，表示『還不止』的意思。

譯: 他的用功是我的三倍還不止。

第一步: He studies hard.

第二步: He studies <u>as</u> hard <u>as</u> I.

第三步: He studies <u>three times</u> <u>as</u> hard <u>as</u> I.

第四步: He studies <u>more than</u> <u>three times</u> <u>as</u> hard <u>as</u> I.

同理: I am <u>more than</u> <u>three times</u> <u>as</u> old <u>as</u> he.
(我的年齡是他的三倍還不止。)

注意:
more than + 倍數 + as...as
= 倍數 + more...than

故: He is <u>more than</u> <u>three times</u> <u>as</u> diligent <u>as</u> I.
= He is <u>three times</u> <u>more</u> diligent <u>than</u> I.

He studies <u>more than</u> <u>three times</u> <u>as</u> hard <u>as</u> I.
= He studies <u>three times</u> <u>harder</u> <u>than</u> I.
注意:
hard 的比較級為 harder,而非 more hard。

I am <u>more than</u> <u>three times</u> <u>as</u> old <u>as</u> he.
= I am <u>three times</u> <u>older</u> <u>than</u> he.
注意:
old 的比較級為 older,而非 more old。

d.

倍數詞 + { the / that / this / those / these / 所有格 } + 名詞　　是……的幾倍

本句構必須要與名詞並用。

譯: 他的錢是我的兩倍。

第一步: 先譯『他有我的錢。』

He has <u>my</u> money.
得知有<u>所有格</u> my

第二步: 再將倍數詞置於所有格之前，即完成整句的翻譯。
He has <u>twice</u> <u>my</u> money.
　　　　<u>倍數詞</u> <u>所有格</u>

同理: 這條河的長度是淡水河的十倍。
The river is <u>ten times</u> <u>the</u> length of the
　　　　　　　倍數詞
Tamsui River.
= The river is <u>ten times</u> <u>as</u> long <u>as</u> the Tamsui
River.

e. more than + 倍數詞 + the (或 所有格) + 名詞
是……的幾倍還不止

本句構與 d.中的句構大致一樣，只是在倍數詞之前加了
more than，表示『還不止』的意思。

譯: 他的錢是我的兩倍還不止。

第一步: He has my money.
第二步: He has twice my money.
第三步: He has more than twice my money.

同理: The river is more than ten times the length of
the Tamsui River.
(這條河的長度是淡水河的十倍還不止。)

f. 下列詞類均可視為倍數詞:
one-third　　　三分之一
two-thirds　　三分之二
　　:　　　　　:
　　:　　　　　:
three-fourths　四分之三
　　:　　　　　:

```
        :                    :
one-fifth            五分之一
two-fifths           五分之二
        :                    :
        :                    :
   twice             二倍
three times          三倍
four times           四倍
        :                    :
        :                    :
```

例: I am half as old as you.
(我的年齡只有你的一半。)

I study only one-third as hard as he.
(我僅及他三分之一用功。)

She has twice my weight.
(她的體重有我的兩倍。)

g. 特殊句構:

(1) twice as...as 　　是……的兩倍
  = as...again as
    例: He is twice as old as I.
      = He is as old again as I.
        (他的年紀是我的兩倍。)

      He has twice as much money as I.
    = He has as much money again as I.
      (他的錢是我的兩倍。)

(2) half as...again as 　　是……的一倍半
  = one and a half times as...as

    例: He is eight years old, and I am half as
        old again as he.

（他八歲，我十二歲。）

(3) as many as ＋ 數字 ＋ 複數名詞　　多達……

例：As many as 100 people were killed in the air crash.
（這次空難中多達一百人喪生。）

There are as many as five apples on the table.
（桌上的蘋果有五個之多。）

但：He has as much as five dollars with him.
（○）
（他身上有五塊錢之多。）
He has as many as five dollars with him.
（×）

理由：
five dollars 固然爲複數名詞，但其集合名詞爲 money，是不可數名詞，修飾 money 要說 much money，而非 many money。故使用 as...as 時，亦要用 as much as ＋ 金錢名詞。

例：Building costs ran up to as much as NT$ 20 million.
（建築費用漲到高達台幣兩千萬元。）

同理：
as long as ＋ 數字 ＋ 名詞	長達
as wide as ＋ 數字 ＋ 名詞	寬達
as high as ＋ 數字 ＋ 名詞	高達
as early as ＋ 數字 ＋ 名詞	早在
as late as ＋ 數字 ＋ 名詞	遲在

例：I have been learning English (for) as long as 25 years.

（我學英文已有二十五年之久。）

He came home as late as two in the morning.
（他遲至清晨兩點才回家。）

The river is as wide as 100 meters.
（這條河寬達一百公尺。）

I mailed the letter as early as Friday.
（我早在星期五就把信寄了。）

8. not so much...as...
　與其說是……倒不如說是……

a. 表『與其說是……倒不如說是……』，共有四種用法：
  (1) not so + │adj.│ + as │adj.│
              │adv.│   │adv.│

  (2) not so much + n. + as + n.

  (3) not so much + │介系詞片語│ + as + │介系詞片語│
                    │不定詞片語│   │不定詞片語│

  (4) not so much + 動詞 + as + 動詞

b. not so + │adj.│ + as │adj.│
            │adv.│   │adv.│

由於形容詞或副詞不能以 much 修飾，故不可用 not so much + adj. / adv. + as，而要用 not so + adj. / adv. + as 的句構。

例: She is not so beautiful as charming.
            　　形容詞　　　　　形容詞
  = She is charming rather than beautiful.
  （與其說她美，不如說她迷人。）

注意:
本句構亦可改寫成:
She is not beautiful so much as charming.

c. not so much + n. + as + n.

例: He is not so much a writer as a scholar.
　　　　　　　　　　名詞　　　　　名詞
　= He is a scholar rather than a writer.
　(與其說他是個作家，不如說他是個學者。)

　He is not so much a genius as an idiot.
　　　　　　　　　　名詞　　　　　名詞
　= He is an idiot rather than a genius.
　(與其說他是天才，不如說他是白癡。)

d. not so much + | 介系詞片語 | + as + | 介系詞片語 |
　　　　　　　　　| 不定詞片語 |　　　　| 不定詞片語 |

例: Success lies not so much in luck as in hard work.
　　　　　　　　　　　　　　　　介系詞片語 介系詞片語
　= Success lies in hard work rather than (in) luck.
　(與其說成功在於運氣不如說在於辛勤努力。)

　Our success was attributed not so much to your
　　　　　　　　　　　　　　　　　　　　　　介系詞片語
　help as to our cooperation.
　　　　　　介系詞片語
　= Our success was attributed to our cooperation
　rather than (to) your help.
　(我們的成功與其歸功於你的幫忙，不如說是我們的合
　作。)

　The great use of a school education is not so
　much to teach you things as to teach you the
　　　　　不定詞片語　　　　　　　不定詞片語

art of learning.
= The great use of a school education is to teach
you the art of learning <u>rather than</u> to teach
you things.
（學校教育的最大用處，與其說是教你東西，不如說是
教你學習的方法。）

e. not so much + 動詞 + as + 動詞

例: The oceans do <u>not so much</u> <u>divide</u> the world <u>as</u>
　　　　　　　　　　　　　　　 動詞
<u>unite</u> it.
動詞
= The oceans do <u>not</u> divide the world <u>so much as</u>
unite it.

= The oceans unite the world <u>rather than</u> divide
it.
（與其說是海洋分割這個世界，不如說是統合這個世
界。）

f. not so much as...　　　甚至都不
= not even...
本片語使用時，要置於助動詞之後，即
cannot so much as + 原形動詞　　　甚至……都不能
do not so much as + 原形動詞　　　甚至……都不
have not so much as + 過去分詞　　　甚至……都沒有

例: He <u>cannot so much as</u> <u>write</u> his own name.
= He <u>cannot even</u> <u>write</u> his own name.
（他甚至連自己的名字都不會寫。）

He <u>did not so much as</u> <u>thank</u> me.
= He <u>did not even</u> <u>thank</u> me.
（他甚至都沒謝我。）

He <u>has not so much as</u> <u>written</u> a single word yet.

= He <u>has not even written</u> a single word yet.
（他甚至連半個字都還沒寫。）

注意:
介系詞 without 之後亦可採用類似片語，即:
without so much as + Ving
= without even + Ving

例: He went away without so much as saying good-bye.
　= He went away without even saying good-bye.
（他走了，連『再見』都沒說。）

9. the + 比較級..., the + 比較級...
　a. 句型分析:

例: The older he grew, the weaker his memory became.
（他愈老，記憶力愈差。）

此為表『愈……就愈……』的句型，茲分析如下:
The| older he grew,
　　└ 副詞子句
　↓
副詞連接詞，引導副詞子句。

The 不具任何意義，故不必譯出。但 The 亦兼副詞，修飾其後的比較級形容詞 older。

the| weaker his memory became.
　　└ 主要子句
　↓
副詞，亦不具任何意義，修飾其後的比較級形容詞 weaker。

　b.『愈……就愈……』的造句法:

由於 The..., the... 均為副詞，故使用本句型的先決條件為:
句中要有副詞或形容詞。

譯: 你愈用功，就愈能成爲一個好學生。

第一步: 加入 The..., the..., 並於 The 及 the 之後預留空白, 即:
The _____..., the _____....

第二步: 將要譯的中文句子『愈』去掉, 而成:
你用功, 你將成爲一個好學生。
You study hard, you'll become a good student.

第三步: 將第二步中的英文句子置於第一步中的空格, 而成:
The _____ you study <u>hard</u>, the _____ you'll
　　　　　　　　　　　副詞
become a <u>good</u> student.
　　　　　　形容詞

第四步: 將第三步句中的形容詞或副詞移位到空格中, 並變成比較級。若形容詞之後有名詞, 該名詞也要移位, 而原有冠詞 a 或 an 則刪除, 即:
The _____ you study <u>hard</u>,
　　　↑　　　　　　　　副詞
the _____ you'll become a <u>good student</u>.
　　↑↑　　　　　　　　　　形容詞 名詞

→ The harder you study, the better student you'll become.

爲了使同學能夠牢記這種造句法, 雄雄老師特別設計了下列公式:
(1) 加 The _____, the _____;
(2) 造句子;
(3) 在空格之後填上句子;
(4) 副詞或形容詞往前移入空格中; 若形容詞之後有名詞, 也往前移, 但名詞若有冠詞則要刪除。

譯: 你愈謹慎，犯的錯就愈少。

第一步: The _____..., the ____....

第二步: 你謹慎，你犯的錯就少。
You are <u>careful</u>, you'll make <u>few</u> mistakes.

第三步: The _____ you are careful, the ____ you'll
　　　　　　　　　　　 形容詞

　　　　make <u>few</u> <u>mistakes</u>.
　　　　　　形容詞　名詞

第四步: The <u>more careful</u> you are, the <u>fewer mistakes</u>
　　　　you'll make.

c. 使用『愈……就愈……』的句構，要注意兩點:
(1) 若句中無副詞或形容詞，則在 The 或 the 之後放副
　　詞 more 或 less。
　　譯: 你愈愛我，我就對你愈好。
　　The _____ you love me, the _____ I'll be
　　　　　　　　無形容詞或副詞

　　<u>nice</u> to you.
　　形容詞
　→ The <u>more</u> you love me, the <u>nicer</u> I'll be
　　to you.

(2) 若句中的主詞為一般名詞，而非代名詞 (he, it, you
　　they,...) 或專有名詞 (John, Mary...)，且後面的動
　　詞為 be 動詞時，該 be 動詞可省略。

　　例: The better <u>the boy</u> (is), the more I like
　　　　　　　　　 一般名詞

　　him. (〇)
　　(這男孩愈好，我愈喜歡他。)

| The better | you, 代名詞 John, 專有名詞 | the more I like | you. (×) him. (×) |

→ The better you are, the more I like you. (○)
   The better John is, the more I like him. (○)
   (你／約翰 愈好，我就愈喜歡 你／約翰。)

故: The colder the weather (is), the more
            一般名詞
   comfortable my life (will be). (○)
                   一般名詞

即: The colder the weather, the more comfortable
   my life.
   (天氣愈冷，我生活就愈舒服。)

d. 比較級 + and + 比較級　　愈來愈……

例: It is getting warmer and warmer in spring.
   (在春天，氣候變得愈來愈暖和了。)

   The girl became more and more beautiful.
   (這女孩變得愈來愈漂亮。)

   You should study harder and harder.
   (你應該更用功唸書。)

e. all the + 比較級 + | for + N
                        | because 子句
   即令……卻更加……
   就是因為……卻更加……

   本片語中的 for 為介系詞，之後接名詞為其受詞。because
   則為副詞連接詞，引導副詞子句。for 及 because 原本表
   『因為』，但在此句型中，老手的翻譯家均譯成『即使』或

『即令』，更吻合英文的意思。

例: I like her <u>well</u>.
　　　　　　副詞

→ I like her <u>all the better</u> | because she is poor.
　　　　　　　　　　　　　　　 | for her poverty.

　(即使她窮，我卻更喜歡她。)

　　I like her very <u>much</u>.
　　　　　　　　　副詞

→ I like her <u>all the more</u> because she is poor.

　(即使她窮，我卻更喜歡她。)

　　He studied <u>hard</u>.
　　　　　　　副詞

→ He studied <u>all the harder</u> | because he had failed.
　　　　　　　　　　　　　　　 | for his failure.

　(即使他失敗了，他卻更用功唸書。)

　　She is <u>beautiful</u>.
　　　　　　形容詞

→ She is <u>all the more beautiful</u>
　|because her clothing is shabby.
　|for her shabby clothing.

　(即使她的衣著襤褸，卻顯得更美麗了。)

f. none the + 比較級 + |because 子句　　即使……卻一點也不
　　　　　　　　　　　 |for + N

例: His health is not <u>good</u>.
　　　　　　　　　　　形容詞

→ His health is <u>none the better</u>
　|for his exercise.
　|because he takes exercise.

　(即使他運動，健康狀況卻一點也不好。)

　　　　She is not beautiful.
　　　　　　　　形容詞
　　　　She is none the more beautiful because she wears
　　　　a fancy dress.
　　　　(即使她身穿時髦洋裝，仍是一點也不漂亮。)

g. none the less + |adj.| + |because 子句　　即使……卻仍然
　　　　　　　　　 |adv.|　　|for + N

　　none the less 為副詞，原意為『一點也不少』，譯成『仍
　　然』。可修飾動詞、形容詞或副詞。

　　(1) 修飾動詞，置於該動詞之後。
　　　　例: I love him none the less because he is poor.
　　　　　　及物動詞 ◄─────────┘
　　　　　　(即使他窮，我還是一樣愛他。)

　　(2) 修飾形容詞，置於該形容詞之前。
　　　　例: She is none the less beautiful for her
　　　　　　　　　 └────────►形容詞
　　　　　　shabby clothing.
　　　　　　(即使她的衣著襤褸，卻依然美麗。)

　　(3) 修飾副詞，置於該副詞之前。
　　　　例: He studied none the less hard because he had
　　　　　　　　　　　　　 └────────►副詞
　　　　　　failed.
　　　　　　(即使他失敗了，卻仍然用功唸書。)

10. no more...than　　不是……正如……不是……
　　　no less...than　　和……一樣
　　a. 此類句構一共有四種:
　　　(1) no more...than　　……不是……正如……不是……
　　　　　例: He is no more a student than I (am).
　　　　　　　(他不是學生正如我也不是學生一樣。)

(2) no less...than 和……一樣

例: He is <u>no less</u> good at English <u>than</u> John (is).
(他和約翰一樣精通英文。)

(3) not more...than 沒有比……更……

例: She is <u>not more</u> beautiful <u>than</u> Mary (is).
(她沒有瑪莉漂亮。)

(4) not less...than 至少與……一樣

例: She is <u>not less</u> beautiful <u>than</u> Mary (is).
(她至少與瑪莉一樣美。)

b. no more....than ……不是……正如……不是……
本句構係由下列句型演變而成:

譯: 他不會唱歌,正如我也不會唱歌一樣。

(1) He <u>cannot</u> sing, <u>just as</u> I cannot sing.

(2) He cannot sing <u>not any more than</u> I cannot sing.
沒有比……多
(即 與……一樣/正如……)

但: (a) 因為在 He ca<u>nnot</u> sing 一句中已有 not,故 not
any more than 中的 not 要省略,以避免雙重否定
,而成 any more than,仍譯成『與……一樣』或
『正如』。

(b) than 之後的相同詞類要省略,故 than I cannot
sing 中的 not 要省略,而成 than I can sing,
由於 He cannot sing 中已有 sing,故 than I
can sign 中的 sing 要省略,而成 than I (can)。

即: He cannot sing ~~not~~ any more than I
~~cannot sing~~.

= He cannot sing <u>any more</u> than <u>I (can)</u>.
　　　正如　　　　　我不會唱歌

(3) 在 He cannot sing any more than I (can). 的句構
　　中，any more 可移位至 cannot 之後，any 與 not 結
　　合，而形成 no, 後面再接 more。

即: He cannot <u>any more</u> sing <u>than</u> I (can).

　　　　　結合成 no
　= He can <u>no more</u> sing <u>than</u> I (can).
　　(他不會唱歌，正如我也不會唱歌一樣。)

換言之，下列三句意思均相同:

He cannot sing, <u>just as</u> I <u>cannot sing</u>.
= He cannot sing <u>any more</u> than I (can).
= He can <u>no more</u> sing <u>than</u> I (can).

譯: 鯨魚不是魚，正如馬不是魚一樣。
　　A whale is <u>not</u> a fish, <u>just as</u> a horse <u>is not</u>
　　<u>a fish</u>.
　= A whale is <u>not</u> a fish n~~ot~~ any more than a
　　horse is <u>not</u> a f~~ish~~.
　　(同詞類要省略)

　　整理:
　　A whale is <u>not</u> a fish any more <u>than</u> a horse is.
　= A whale is <u>no more</u> a fish <u>than</u> a horse is.

注意:
(a) 在 no more...than 或 not...any more than 的句
　　構中，若 than 之後的詞類不同於前面的詞類時，
　　則不可省略。

　　譯: 他不會唱歌，正如我不會跳舞一樣。

He cannot <u>sing</u>, just as I cannot <u>dance</u>.

= He cannot <u>sing</u> any more than I cannot dance.

相同詞類要省略

不同詞類要保留

整理：

He cannot sing <u>any more than</u> I can dance.

= He can <u>no more</u> sing <u>than</u> I can dance.

他不是學生，猶如我不是老師一樣。

He is not a <u>student</u>, <u>just as</u> I am not <u>a</u>
<u>teacher</u>.

= He is <u>not a student</u> any more than I am
not a teacher.

整理：

He is not a student any more than I am a
teacher.

= He is no more a student than I am a teacher.

(b) happy, good, clever...等形容詞以及 well,
hard, fast,...等副詞，在比較級中會形成不規
則變化，而成為 happier, better, cleverer...
或 better, harder, faster,...。

故置於 no more 或 not any more 之後時，不可寫成：

no more happy　　　　not any more well

no more good　　　　 not any more hard

no more clever　　　　not any more fast

　　　　∶　　　　　　　　　　∶

　　　　∶　　　　　　　　　　∶

而要寫成：

no happier	no better
no better	no harder
no cleverer	no faster
⋮	⋮
⋮	⋮

譯: 他跑不快，正如我一樣。
He cannot run fast, just as I cannot run fast.
= He cannot run any ~~more fast~~ than I can.
　　　　　　　　　　faster

他的英文不好，就像我一樣。
He is not good at English, just as I am not good at English.
= He is <u>not</u> good at English <u>any more than</u> I am.
= He is <u>no more good</u> at English than I am.
　　　　　　／better

c. no less...than　　和……一樣
= as... as
由於 no less...than 就等於 as...as，故 no less 之後可置副詞或形容詞修飾。
(1) 副詞:

例: He studies <u>no less hard than</u> John.
　　　　　　　　　副詞
= He studies <u>as hard as</u> John.
(他和約翰一樣用功。)

(2) 形容詞:

例: He is <u>no less good</u> at English <u>than</u> John.
　　　　　　　　形容詞
= He is <u>as good</u> at English <u>as</u> John.

（他和約翰一樣精通英文。）

d. not more...than　　　沒有比……更多
 = at best as...as　　　最多只是和……一樣
本句構較為簡單，在 more...than（比……更）之前加上 not
即可。

例：She is <u>more</u> beautiful <u>than</u> Mary.
　　（她比瑪莉美。）
 → She is <u>not more</u> beautiful <u>than</u> Mary.
 = She is <u>at best</u> as beautiful <u>as</u> Mary.
　　（她不比瑪莉美麗——頂多只是和瑪莉一樣美。）

e. not less...than　　　沒有比……更少
 = at least as...as　　　至少與……一樣

例：She is <u>not less</u> beautiful than Mary.
 = She is <u>at least</u> as beautiful <u>as</u> Mary.
　　（她至少和瑪莉一樣美。）

f. 茲整理本單元句型如下：
例：He is <u>no more</u> handsome <u>than</u> I.
 = He is <u>not</u> handsome <u>any more than</u> I.
　　（他不瀟灑，就如我一樣——兩人都不瀟灑。）

　　He is <u>no less</u> handsome <u>than</u> I.
 = He is <u>as</u> handsome <u>as</u> I.
　　（他和我一樣瀟灑。）

　　He is <u>not more</u> handsome <u>than</u> I.
 = He is <u>at best</u> as handsome <u>as</u> I.
　　（他不比我瀟灑——頂多跟我一樣瀟灑。）

　　He is <u>not less</u> handsome <u>than</u> I.
 = He is <u>at least</u> as handsome <u>as</u> I.
　　（他至少跟我一樣瀟灑。）

11. no more than + 數字詞　　　　僅僅……
　　 no less than + 數字詞　　　　剛剛好……
　　 not more than + 數字詞　　　 最多不超過……
　　 not less than + 數字詞　　　　至少……

　　a. 以上片語，均爲修飾數字詞的副詞片語，句型如下：

　　　(1) <u>no more than</u> + <u>數字詞</u> + N　　　僅僅
　　　　　　 adv.　　　　　a.
　　　 = <u>only</u> + 數字詞 + N

　　　　　例：It is no more than ten minutes' walk from
　　　　　　　here.
　　　　　　　(從這兒走路只需要十分鐘路程。)

　　　(2) <u>no less than</u> + <u>數字詞</u> + N　　　剛好，多達
　　　　　　 adv.　　　　　a.
　　　 = <u>as many as</u> + 數字詞 + N

　　　　　例：It is no less than ten minutes' walk from
　　　　　　　here.
　　　　　　　(從這兒走路剛好要十分鐘路程。)

　　　(3) <u>not more than</u> + <u>數字詞</u> + N　　　最多不超過
　　　　　　 adv.　　　　　a.
　　　 = <u>at most</u> + 數字詞 + N

　　　　　例：I'll stay here not more than three days.
　　　　　　　(我將待在這裡最多不超過三天。)

　　　(4) <u>not less than</u> + <u>數字詞</u> + N　　　至少
　　　　　　 adv.　　　　　a.
　　　 = <u>at least</u> + 數字詞 + N

　　　　　例：I'll stay here not less than three days.
　　　　　　　(我將待在這裡至少三天。)

b. at most / at best 的用法比較:
   (1) at most + 數字詞　　最多不超過
     = not more than

   例: He is at most ten years old.
   (他最多只有十歲。)

   (2) at best 充其量　　只不過是
     = nothing but

   例: He is at best a student.
   (他只不過是個學生。)
     = He is nothing but a student.
     = He is but a student.
     = He is only a student.

c. much more...　　更不用說……

   例: She can speak French, much more English.
   (她會說法語,更不用說英語了。)

   注意:
   此類用法有『肯定』與『否定』之別。

   (1) 肯定句:

She can speak French,	not to mention writing it.
	not to speak of writing it.
	to say nothing of writing it.
	let alone write it.
	much more write it.
	still more write it.

   (她會說法語,更不用說寫法文了。)

   注意:
   not to mention, not to speak of, to say nothing of
   之後接名詞或動名詞為其受詞。但 let alone, much more

及 still more 則有對等連接詞的意味，連接對等的詞類。
本句中 She can speak French...中的 speak 爲原形動詞
故 let alone, much more, still more 之後接原形動詞。

例: You have a right <u>to your property</u>,
介詞片語

	let alone
	much more
	still more

<u>to your ideas</u>.
介詞片語
(你對於自己的財產有權利，更不用說對於你的構
想了。)

I enjoy <u>dancing</u>,　| let alone | <u>listening</u> to music.
動名詞　　　　| much more | 動名詞
　　　　　　　| still more |

(我喜歡跳舞，更不用說聽音樂了。)

(2) 否定句:

	not to mention writing it.
	not to speak of writing it.
She cannot speak French,	to say nothing of writing it.
	let alone write it.
	much less write it.
	still less write it.

(她不會說法語，更不用說寫法文了。)

注意:
由此得知 not to mention, not to speak of, to say
nothing of, let alone 可用於肯定句、否定句中。
much more, still more 只用於肯定句。much less,
still less 只用於否定句。

12. 本節第7至11項摘自常春藤叢書『英文活用句型翻譯』第
344頁至380頁。

Exercise

Ⅰ. 請選出一個正確的答案:

1. He is _____ than the two boys.
   (A) better
   (B) more good
   (C) the better
   (D) the best

2. He is _____ of the two boys.
   (A) better
   (B) more good
   (C) the better
   (D) the best

3. He is _____ boy than Tom.
   (A) better
   (B) a better
   (C) the better
   (D) the best

4. Your knowledge is greater than a _____.
   (A) specialist
   (B) specialist's
   (C) specialists
   (D) specialists'

5. My watch is more expensive than _____.
   (A) you
   (B) your
   (C) yours
   (D) yourself

6. Mary is _____ than her sister.
   (A) less kinder
   (B) kind
   (C) less kind
   (D) more kinder

7. Smith is not so _____ as you are.
   (A) strong
   (B) stronger
   (C) strongest
   (D) the strong

8. Jean is taller than _____ in her class.
   (A) all girls
   (B) all the girls
   (C) any other girl
   (D) any girl

9. New York City is larger than _____ city in the U.S.
   - (A) any
   - (B) all
   - (C) any other
   - (D) all the other

10. New York City is larger than _____ city in Taiwan.
    - (A) any
    - (B) all
    - (C) any other
    - (D) all the other

11. Helen is _____ than her sister.
    - (A) more proud
    - (B) proud
    - (C) prouder
    - (D) the proudest

12. Helen is _____ than vain.
    - (A) more proud
    - (B) proud
    - (C) prouder
    - (D) the proudest

13. John seems to be _____ than wise.
    - (A) clever
    - (B) cleverer
    - (C) more clever
    - (D) the cleverer

14. Knowledge is the most useful thing. = _____
    - (A) No thing is so useful as knowledge.
    - (B) Knowledge is more useful than most things.
    - (C) Nothing is more useful than knowledge.
    - (D) Knowledge is more useful than all things.

15. To talk too much is sometimes _____ than useful.
    - (A) worse
    - (B) bad
    - (C) more bad
    - (D) much worse

16. I did not run so fast as he. = _____.
    - (A) He ran faster than I.
    - (B) I ran most fast.
    - (C) He ran fastest than I.
    - (D) He ran fast than I.

17. Mary knows electronics _____ than any of her classmates.
    (A) well   (B) better   (C) best   (D) betterly

18. Most of us work _____ in the morning than in the after-
    noon.
    (A) efficient   (B) efficiently
    (C) more efficient   (D) more efficiently

19. Minneapolis is now _____ of these two competing cities.
    (A) the largest   (B) the large
    (C) the larger   (D) larger

20. Sound travels _____ air.
    (A) faster through water than through
    (B) faster than through water and
    (C) through water faster and
    (D) where it is faster through water than through

21. Few of the people who live on the cooperatives _____
    than they were as laborers.
    (A) is well off financial
    (B) financially well off
    (C) are better off financially
    (D) financial better off

22. The photographs of Mars taken by satellites are _____
    than those taken from the Earth.
    (A) clearest   (B) the clearest
    (C) much clearer   (D) more clearer

23. Adams now maintains that it is less important to save
    the nation _____.
    (A) had alerted them to a perilous future
    (B) from alerting it to a perilous future
    (C) as to alert them to a perilous future
    (D) than to alert it to a perilous future

24. I think Alice's _____ than unfriendly.
    (A) shy   (B) shyer
    (C) more shy   (D) more shy rather

25. Microwave oven thermometers are _____ than other kinds of oven thermometers.
    (A) more cost   (B) more costly
    (C) more costlier   (D) less cost

標準答案：1.(A) 2.(C) 3.(B) 4.(B) 5.(C) 6.(C) 7.(A)
        8.(C) 9.(C) 10.(A) 11.(C) 12.(A) 13.(C) 14.(C)
        15.(C) 16.(A) 17.(B) 18.(D) 19.(C) 20.(A) 21.(C)
        22.(C) 23.(D) 24.(C) 25.(B)

習題解答：

1. 一般的比較級用法。

2. the + 比較級 + of + 二者   二者中較……的

3. boy 為可數名詞，故 better boy 之前應加 a。

4. Your knowledge is greater than a specialist's knowledge.
→ Your knowledge is greater than a specialist's.

5. My watch is more expensive than your watch.
  = My watch is more expensive than yours.

6. less 之後必須加原級形容詞。

7. as + 原級形容詞 + as...   和……一樣……
    not so + 原級形容詞 + as...   沒有比……更……
  = less + 原級形容詞 + than...

    例：John is as tall as you.
       （約翰和你一樣高。）

```
        John  is  not  so  diligent  as  you.
     =  John  is  less  diligent  than  you.
        （約翰沒有你用功。）
```

8．Jean 和其班級作比較時，必須將自身與班級分開，故指班上
女生用 any other girl in her class。

9．New York City 本身是美國都市之一，故與美國其他都市比較
時，必須用 any other city in the U.S.。

10．New York City 並非台灣的都市之一，故與台灣的都市比較時
，不必加入 other。

11．一般的比較句構。

12．本身的性質作比較時，一律用 more + 原級形容詞。
more A than B　　與其說是 B，不如說是 A
= less B than A
= not so A as B

例：John is more lazy than stupid.
= John is less stupid than lazy.
= John is not so stupid as lazy.
（說約翰笨，不如說他懶。）

13．與上題同理。

14．Knowledge is the most useful thing.
= Nothing is | so useful as | knowledge.
             | more useful than |
= Knowledge is more useful than | all the other things.
                                | any other thing.

15．與第十二題同理。

16．not so + 原級副詞 + as　　沒有比……更……

= less ＋ 原級副詞 ＋ than

１７．此處 better 做比較級副詞，修飾 knows。

１８．比較級副詞用法

１９．與第二題同理。

２０．Sound travels faster through water than it travels through air.
→ Sound travels faster through water than through air.

２１．well off　　境況佳的

２２．修飾比較級形容詞要用 much，不可用 more。

２３．...it is less important to save...than it is to alert...
= ...it is less important to save...than to alert...

２４．與第十二題同理。

２５．costly 爲形容詞，表『昂貴的』。

心得欄

第十一章　代名詞

1. it 作虛主詞

a. 代替不定詞片語

例: It is good to study.
（讀書有益。）
但不定詞本身可作主詞，故上句可改為：
To study is good.

It is necessary to read these books.
= To read these books is (非 are) necessary.
（這些書必須唸。）
注意:
books 雖為複數，然其並非主詞，主詞乃整個不定詞片語，故動詞仍用單數。

b. 代替 that 子句(名詞子句)

例: It is good that he can study.
= That he can study is good.
（他能讀書，這是件好事。）
（名詞子句本身具有名詞的功能，故可作主詞）
He can study is good.(×)
（He can study 是句子，非名詞子句，因 He 之前無連接詞，不能構成名詞子句，故不能作主詞）

c. 代替動名詞
這種用法只有與極少數名詞連用。

例: It is ｜ no use ｜ reading novels all day long.
　　　　　｜ no good ｜

= There is no use (in) reading novels all day
　long.
（整天看小說是沒用的。）
It is no use to read novels all day long.(×)
但 It is ｜ of no use ｜ to read novels all day long. (○)
　　　　　｜ useless 　｜

2 . it 作虛受詞:
即 it 作不完全及物動詞之受詞，代替不定詞片語或 that
子句。

a. 動詞若加受詞意思很完整，而無須補充說明時，謂完全及
物動詞。

例: I love him.
（我愛他。）

但動詞雖加受詞，意思卻不完整，而需要補充說明，謂
『不完全及物動詞』，其補充語一定是名詞或形容詞(包
括分詞變成的形容詞)。

例: I think him. (×)
（我認為他。）
　上例句意思殘缺，故需補充語。
　I think him good.(○)
　　　　　　　　adj.
（我認為他人很好。）

　I think him a good man.(○)
　　　　　　　　　n.
（我認為他是個好人。）

　I think him happily.(×)
　　　　　　　adv.

→I think him happy.
（我認為他很快樂。）

b. 不定詞或 that 子句有名詞的功能，可作主詞（如 1 ）亦可
作受詞。

例: I want to go.
　　　　 受詞

　 I think that he is good.
　　　　　 受　　　詞

但兩者卻不能直接作不完全及物動詞之受詞，必須用 it
代替。

例: I think that he is good true.(×)
　　　　　 受　　詞　　補語
→ I think it true that he is good.(○)
　 不完全 vt.
　 （我認為他人的確是不錯。）

　 I think to get up early good. 　(×)
　　　　　 受　　　詞　　補語
→ I think it good to get up early.(○)
　 不完全 vt.
　 （我認為早起很好。）

　 I think (that) it is true that he is good.(○)
　 完全 vt.名詞子句作 think 的受詞

3 . it 用以強調主詞或受詞:

例: I love him.
→ It is I who (或 that) love him.
（愛他的是我。）
His words made me angry.

→ It was his words that (或 which) made me angry.
(使我生氣的是他的話。)

I am in need of your help.

→ It is your help that (或 which) I am in need of.
(我需要的是你的協助。)

4．it 用以強調介詞片語或副詞子句，其結構如下：

It is (was) + | 介詞片語 | + that 子句
            | 副詞子句 |

例: It was in 1974 that I began to study English.
(我是在一九七四年開始學英文的。)

It was because he was lazy that he failed.
(他是因爲懶惰的關係而失敗的。)

5． | most
   | all
   | some
   | any
   | half   of + the (或 my, your...)
   | part
   | the rest
   | two-thirds
   | none

+ | 單數名詞 + 單數動詞 |
   | 複數名詞 + 複數動詞 |

例: Most of the money was stolen.
(money 不可數, 故用 was)
(大部分的錢都被竊了。)
The most of the money was stolen.
(×, 此類代名詞前不得加冠詞)

Some of the students are here.

　　　　(students 爲複數名詞，故用 are)
　　　　(部分學生在這兒。)

　　　　All of students are here.
　　　　(×，缺少 the)
　　　　All of the students are here.(○)
　　　　(所有學生都在這兒。)

　　　　All of his students are here.(○)
　　　　(他所有的學生都在這兒。)

6．almost, most, all 之關係:

almost 爲副詞，不能當代名詞。

most 爲形容詞、副詞，亦可做代名詞。
all 爲形容詞，亦可做代名詞。可由 almost 修飾。

例: Almost of the students are here.(×)
　　Most of the students are here.(○)
　　(大多數學生在這兒。)

　　All of the students are here.(○)
　　(所有的學生都在這兒。)

　　Almost all of the students are here.(○)
　　(幾乎所有的學生都在這兒。)

7．人稱代名詞:

	主格	所有格 (加名詞)	受格	所有格 (不加 名詞)	反身代名詞
第一人稱	I we	my our	me us	mine ours	myself ourselves

第二人稱	you (你)	your	you	yours	yourself
	you (你們)	your	you	yours	yourselves
第三人稱	he	his	him	his	himself
	she	her	her	hers	herself
	it	its	it	its	itself
	they	their	them	theirs	themselves

例: He is a student.(主詞用主格)
(他是學生。)

I like him.(受詞用受格)
(我喜歡他。)

She killed herself.
(主詞受詞同一人，則受詞用反身代名詞)
(她自殺了。)

Her books are interesting.
(所有格 + N)
(她的書很有趣。)

Her books are as interesting as mine.
(避免重複，用所有格代名詞)　　(= my books)
(她的書和我的一樣有趣。)

8．反身代名詞的強勢用法:

例: He himself did it.(強調主詞)
= He did it himself.
(他親自做這件事。)

I want to see the boss himself.(強調受詞)
(我要見老板本人。)

Himself did it.
(×，反身代名詞不能作主詞)

9．that (表單數)，those (表複數)代替前面所提到的名詞，以避免重複。

例：People in Taiwan lead a much better life than people in mainland China. (劣)
People in Taiwan lead a much better life than those in mainland China.　　(佳)
(台灣的百姓要比大陸百姓過著更富裕的生活。)

The color of this door is more beautiful than the color of that window.　(劣)
The color of this door is more beautiful than that of that window.　(佳)
(這扇門的顏色比那扇窗的好看多了。)

10．

a any some this these that those which a few	＋名詞＋of	mine yours his theirs ： ： Peter's Mary's	或 of	my own your own his own their own ： ： Peter's own Mary's own

例：He is a friend of mine.(○)
He is a friend of me.(×)
(他是我的一位朋友。)

11．...those | who
whom | ...(○)
...them | who
whom | ...(×)

例：Tell those who are late to come and see me.(○)
（叫那些遲到的人來見我。）

Evan's paintings are interesting to them who believe
in nihilism.　　　　　(×)
→ Evan's paintings are interesting to those who
believe in nihilism. (○)
（伊凡的畫引起虛無主義者的興趣。）

1 2 . Every man and woman should do <u>his</u> best to protect his
country.(不能用 their)
（不分男女都應盡力保衛自己的國家。）

One should do <u>one's</u> （美語中可用 his） duty.
（人人都應克盡己責。）

1 3 . a. each other 　　（兩者互相）
one another 　　（三者以上互相）

例：The two students like each other.
（這兩位同學彼此都很喜歡對方。）

The five students hate one another.
（這五位同學彼此討厭。）
注意：
each other 與 one another 在美語中已漸可通用。

b. one after the other 　　（兩者相繼地）
one after another 　　（三者以上相繼地）

例：He raised his hands one after the other.
（他輪流舉起左右手。）

All the students came in one after another.
（所有學生一個接一個地進來。）

14. either　（兩者中任一）　any　（三者以上任一）
　　　neither（兩者皆不）　　none（三者以上皆不）
　　　both　　（兩者皆）　　　all　（三者以上皆）

例: I don't care whether you have coffee or tea; either
will do.
（你有咖啡也好，茶也好，我都不在乎，隨便那樣都行。）

Neither of the two books is good.
（這兩本書都不好。）

None of the three students is（或 are）diligent.
（三個學生中沒有一個是用功的。）

Both of the two students are lazy.
（兩個學生都懶惰。）

All of the five apples are rotten.
（五個蘋果都爛掉了。）

I don't like any of the four chairs.
（四把椅子沒有一把是我喜歡的。）

Exercise

I. 請選出一個正確的答案:

1. I guess James didn't have a chance to win the election.
   _____ the people in the city voted for his opponent.
   (A) Almost all of   (B) Most all of
   (C) Most of all   (D) Almost the whole of

2. Wagner and Strauss were such good friends that they
   frequently exchanged gifts with _____.
   (A) each one   (B) each other
   (C) the other   (D) another

3. The beginning course in algebra was very easy, but
   _____ one is certainly not.
   (A) which   (B) this   (C) some   (D) no

4. She is very forgetful and cannot recognize her grand-
   children from one visit to _____.
   (A) next one   (B) other one
   (C) the other one   (D) the next

5. Even though Africa game preserves have saved many
   animals, there are _____ that will not be saved.
   (A) some more   (B) all others
   (C) many more   (D) much more

6. Some of our wedding vows were taken from the tradi-
   tional ceremony, and some of them were written by
   _____.
   (A) my husband and I   (B) my husband and my

(C) my husband and me　　(D) my husband and mine

7. The principal responsibility of managing the dormitory rests with the students ＿＿＿＿.
(A) itself　　　　　　　(B) of itself
(C) themselves　　　　　(D) their selves

8. John behaved so strangely today; I thought he wasn't acting like ＿＿＿＿.
(A) him　　(B) himself　　(C) he would　　(D) he does

9. I don't take John's pen because I don't like ＿＿＿＿.
(A) that pen of his　　　(B) that his pen
(C) his that pen　　　　(D) that pen of him

Ⅱ. 請選出錯誤的劃線部分：

10. As one nears the bridge, you come to a narrow rocky
　　　　A　　　　　　　　　　　　　　　　　　　　B
valley, the site of several historic battles.
　　　　　C　　　　　　　　　D

11. Many modern skyscrapers, though visually pleasing,
　　　　　　　　　　　　　　　　　　A
they have heating and cooling systems that require
　B
closed windows and consequently waste energy.
　C　　　　　　　　　　　　　　　D

12. Each member of the team bought themselves a new
　　　　　　　　　　　　　　A　　　　B
car with the money earned in the championship game.
　　　　　　　　　　　C　　　D

13. The functions performed by individual members of
　　　　　　　　　　　A　　　　　　B

a colony of bees <u>are determined</u> by chemical sub-
　　　　　　　　　 C
stances transferred from <u>a</u> bee to another.
　　　　　　　　　　　　 D

1 4 . They asked us, Henry and <u>I</u>, whether we <u>thought</u> that
　　　　　　　　　　　　　　 A　　　　　　　 B
　　 the statistics <u>had been presented</u> <u>fairly</u> and accu-
　　　　　　　　　　　 C　　　　　　　 D
　　 rately.

1 5 . He is <u>familiar with</u> <u>the most of</u> calculus equations,
　　　　　　 A　　　　　 B
　　 but he wants <u>to study</u> them again <u>before</u> the exami-
　　　　　　　　　 C　　　　　　　　 D
　　 nation.

1 6 . <u>Whoever</u> inspected <u>this</u> radio <u>should have</u> put <u>their</u>
　　 A　　　　　　　 B　　　　 C　　　　 D
　　 identification number on the box.

1 7 . <u>Most</u> early settlers provided for <u>themself</u> <u>before</u>
　　 A　　　　　　　　　　　　　 B　　　 C
　　 sharing their surplus <u>with</u> others.
　　　　　　　　　　　 D

1 8 . Computers are <u>indispensable</u> in data processing, but
　　　　　　　　　 A
　　 some people are afraid that <u>its</u> impersonal solutions
　　　　　　　　　　　　　　　 B
　　 might do <u>harm</u> to mankind <u>in the long run</u>.
　　　　　　 C　　　　　　　 D

1 9 . Maria <u>has long had</u> the desire to become a famous
　　　　　 A

writer <u>even though</u> the study of <u>it</u> would require
　　　　　　B　　　　　　　　　　　C

years of sacrifice <u>on her part</u>.
　　　　　　　　　　　　D

2 0. <u>Every</u> man and woman <u>should vote</u> <u>for</u> the candidate
　　　　A　　　　　　　　　　　B　　　　C

<u>of their choice</u>.
　　　D

2 1. <u>In order to</u> get married in this state, one <u>must</u>
　　　A　　　　　　　　　　　　　　　　　　　　　　B

present a medical report <u>along with</u> <u>your</u> identifi-
　　　　　　　　　　　　　C　　　　　D

cation.

2 2. If we <u>finish</u> all of our business as planned, Helen
　　　　　A

and <u>me</u> will leave <u>for</u> New York <u>on Monday morning</u>.
　　　B　　　　　C　　　　　　　　　D

2 3. William the Conqueror <u>built</u> the Tower of London to
　　　　　　　　　　　　　　A

protect <u>himself</u> from <u>them</u> he <u>had conquered</u>.
　　　　　B　　　　　C　　　　D

2 4. When science, business, and art <u>learn</u> something of
　　　　　　　　　　　　　　　　　　A

<u>each others'</u> methods and goals, the world <u>will have</u>
　　　B　　　　　　　　　　　　　　　　　　C

come <u>closer to</u> cultural harmony.
　　　　D

2 5. She wore clothes <u>that</u> <u>were</u> better than <u>that</u> of the
　　　　　　　　　　A　　B　　　　　　　C

other <u>girls</u>.
　　　　D

26. <u>It</u> is often easier <u>to select</u> a particular tool <u>than</u>
　　 A　　　　　　　　B　　　　　　　　　　　　C
<u>to use</u> <u>them</u> correctly.
　　　　 D

27. <u>It</u> was <u>her</u> <u>who</u> represented her country in the United
　　 A　　 B　 C
Nations and <u>later</u> became ambassador to the United
　　　　　　　 D
States.

28. The speaker announced that <u>there was</u> a small fire
　　　　　　　　　　　　　　　　　 A
and directed <u>them</u> <u>nearest</u> the door <u>to leave first</u>.
　　　　　　　 B　　 C　　　　　　　　　　D

29. While <u>some of</u> lawyers would endorse <u>the opposite</u>
　　　　　 A　　　　　　　　　　　　　　　 B
view, <u>most</u> would probably agree that freedom of
　　　　C
the press <u>is not absolute</u>.
　　　　　　 D

30. The good statesman, <u>like</u> all sensible human beings,
　　　　　　　　　　　　 A
always <u>learns</u> <u>more</u> from <u>their</u> opponents than from
　　　　 B　　 C　　　　 D
his supporters.

標準答案: 1.(A)　2.(B)　3.(B)　4.(D)　5.(C)　6.(C)　7.(C)
　　　　 8.(B)　9.(A) 10.(A) 11.(B) 12.(B) 13.(D) 14.(A)
　　　　 15.(B) 16.(D) 17.(B) 18.(B) 19.(C) 20.(D) 21.(D)
　　　　 22.(B) 23.(C) 24.(B) 25.(C) 26.(D) 27.(B) 28.(B)

29.(A)　30.(D)

習題解說：

1．almost all of the...　　　幾乎所有的……

2．each other　　　彼此(二者)
　　one another　　　彼此(三者以上)

3．關係代名詞 which 本身即為連接詞，其前面不可再加連接詞 but。
　　例: I have a book, which is good. (○)
　　　　I have a book, and which is good. (×)
　　　　I have a book, and it is good. (○)

4．from one visit to the next
　= from one visit to another

5．a. animals 為可數名詞，故其前不可用 much more，而要用 many more。
　　b. some 不可與 more 並用。

6．作 by 的受詞，故用受格 me。

7．students 為複數形，其反身代名詞為 themselves。

8．himself 為 he 的反身受格。

9．所有格不可和指示代名詞 (this, that, these...) 併置於名詞前。
　　his that pen　　(×)
　　that pen of his (○)
　　他的那支筆

10．As one nears 應改為 As you near 使主詞一致。

11. (B) they have 應改爲 have, 因 have 已有主詞 Many modern skyscrapers。

12. (B) themselves 應改爲 himself 或 herself, 因主詞 Each member 是單數。

13. (D) a 應改爲 one (one...another)。

14. (A) I 應改爲 me, 因 Henry and me 係 They asked us 之 受詞同位語, 故用受格。

15. (B) the most of 應改爲 most of the, 或 most, 作形容詞 用, 修飾 calculus equations。

16. (D) their 應改爲 his, 因 whoever = any one who, 恆作單數用。

17. (B) themself 應改爲 themselves。

18. (B) its 應改爲 their, 因 computers 爲複數。

19. (C) it 應改爲 writing, 因 it 不可能代替 a famous writer。

20. (D) their choice 應改爲 his choice, 因 Every man and woman 爲主詞時, 其後代名詞一定是第三人稱單數。
    例: Every man and woman should do his best to
        protect his country.
        (不分男女都應盡力保衛自己的國家。)
        Every teacher and student is here.
        (每一個老師和學生都在這兒。)

21. (D) your 應改爲 his (美語) 或 one's (英語), 因主詞 是 one。
    例: One should love one's country.
        = One should love his country. (較普遍)

2 2. (B) me 應改為 I，作主詞。

2 3. (C) them 應改為 those，因其後有形容詞子句修飾，
...those (whom) he had conquered。

2 4. (B) each others' 應改為 each other's，因 each other
恒無複數。
例: They like each other. (○)
They like each others. (✕)

2 5. (C) that 應改為 those = the clothes。

2 6. (D) them 應改為 it，it = the particular tool。

2 7. (B) her 應改為 she，代名詞作補語時一定要用主格。

2 8. (B) them 應改為 those，those nearest... = those who
were nearest...。

2 9. (A) some of 應改為 some of the 或 some。

3 0. (D) their 應改為 his，因主詞 The good statesman
是單數。

第十二章　反問句

1. 敘述句爲肯定時，接否定反問句；敘述句爲否定時，接肯定反問句。

    a. 敘述句有 be 動詞，反問句沿用 be 動詞。

      例: He is fine, isn't he?

      I wasn't sick, was I?

    b. 敘述句有助動詞，反問句沿用助動詞。

      例: He will come, won't he?

      They can't do it, can they?

      You have done it, haven't you?
      (have 爲助動詞，其後有動詞 done)

    c. 敘述句有一般動詞，反問句則使用 do, does, did。

      例: He came, didn't he?
      (came 爲過去式，故用 didn't)

      He gets up early, doesn't he?
      (gets up 爲現在式，故用 doesn't)

      He didn't come, did he?

      He has a book , doesn't he?
      (has 爲動詞，其後有受詞 a book)

d. 與命令句使用時，反問句一律用 will you。

例: Come here, will you?

　　Stop smoking, will you?

e. 與 Let's...句型使用，反問句一律用 shall we。

例: Let's go, shall we?
　　(咱們走吧，好不好？)

　　Let's not do it, shall we?
　　(咱們別做了，好不好？)

但　Let $\left|\begin{array}{l}\text{us}\\\text{them}\\\text{him}\\\vdots\\\vdots\\\text{John}\end{array}\right|$ go, will you?　(命令句)

　　(請你讓我們走吧，好不好？)

2. 敘述句含有 scarcely, hardly, rarely, no doubt, little, never, by no means, ...等否定副詞，敘述句視為否定句，須接肯定反問句。

例: He $\left|\begin{array}{l}\text{scarcely ever}\\\text{hardly ever}\\\text{almost not ever}\\\text{rarely}\end{array}\right|$ smokes, $\left|\begin{array}{l}\text{does he? (○)}\\\text{doesn't he? (×)}\end{array}\right|$

　　(他很少抽煙，是不是？)

3. 敘述句含有 would rather, ought to, had better,...等助動詞片語，反問句中用其第一個字。

例: I would rather go, | wouldn't I? (○)
                        | wouldn't I rather? (×)

He ought to come, | oughtn't he? (○)
                   | oughtn't he to? (×)

4．否定反問句中，not 的位置:

例: He is bad, | isn't he? (○)
               | is he not? (○)
               | is not he? (×)

He left, | didn't he? (○)
          | did he not? (○)
          | did not he? (×)

5．反問句一定要用代名詞:

例: John is fine, | isn't he?　(○)
                   | isn't John?　(×)

This is not good, | is it?　(○)
                   | is this?　(×)

That is good, | isn't it?　(○)
               | isn't that? (×)

These are not good, | are they?　(○)
                     | are these?　(×)

Those are good, | aren't they?　(○)
                 | aren't those?　(×)

6．敘述句中第一人稱單數主詞 I 表示意見或觀點而有 that 子句時，以 that 子句形成反問句。

例: I | think | that he is nice, | isn't he? (○)
      | believe | | don't I ? (✗)
      | guess |

注意:
但主詞若爲 I 以外的主詞，則反問句仍以敍述句作變化。

例: | We think | that he is nice, | don't we?
    | They think | | don't they?
    | He thinks | | doesn't he?
    | You think | | don't you?
    | : | | :
    | We think | | isn't he? (✗)

Exercise

Ⅰ. 請選出一個正確的答案：

1. He's going to call us back, _____ ?
   (A) won't he   (B) didn't he
   (C) doesn't he   (D) isn't he

2. We had to wait a long time to get our visas, _____ ?
   (A) don't we   (B) didn't we
   (C) couldn't we   (D) shouldn't we

3. She's already made her reservation for next Saturday, _____ ?
   (A) hasn't she   (B) isn't she
   (C) doesn't she   (D) hasn't it

4. They don't seem to answer their phone whenever I call. There isn't anyone at home, _____ ?
   (A) isn't there   (B) is there
   (C) is it   (D) isn't it

5. John isn't a diligent student, for it is the third time he has been late, _____ ?
   (A) wasn't it   (B) hasn't it
   (C) isn't it   (D) hasn't he

6. You haven't seen Mary, _____ ?
   (A) have you   (B) haven't you
   (C) has she   (D) hasn't she

7. You have very little to eat in the morning, _____

you ?
(A) do   (B) don't   (C) have   (D) won't

8 . On this busy road bus drivers ought to be especially careful, _____ ?
(A) ought it   (B) oughtn't they
(C) oughtn't it   (D) don't they

9 . Help me with this box, _____ ?
(A) will you   (B) shall we
(C) shall you   (D) don't you

1 0 . Let's start early, _____ ?
(A) will you   (B) won't you
(C) shall we   (D) will we

1 1 . Let me go home, _____ ?
(A) will you   (B) shall you
(C) shall I   (D) will I

1 2 . Let us go to the movies, _____ ?
(A) shall we   (B) will we
(C) will you   (D) won't we

1 3 . You have a cold bath every morning, _____ you ?
(A) have   (B) haven't   (C) do   (D) don't

1 4 . You'd better go now, _____ you ?
(A) wouldn't   (B) hadn't   (C) would   (D) didn't

1 5 . This is the pen my father gave you, _____ ?
(A) isn't this   (B) didn't he
(C) didn't you   (D) isn't it

1 6 . That's where I used to live when I was a child, _____ ?
(A) isn't that   (B) isn't it

(C) didn't I　　　　　　　　(D) wasn't I

17. But for his accident, he might have been a wonderful pianist, _____ ?
(A) might he　　　　　　　(B) mightn't he
(C) didn't he　　　　　　　(D) wasn't it

18. He never used to get up early, _____ he ?
(A) did　　(B) didn't　　(C) does　　(D) doesn't

19. You can hardly expect me to lend you money again, _____ you ?
(A) can　　(B) can't　　(C) do　　(D) don't

20. Mary seldom goes out in the evening, _____ ?
(A) does she　　　　　　　(B) doesn't she
(C) does Mary　　　　　　　(D) doesn't Mary

21. There's been no man in this house since you left, _____ ?
(A) hasn't there　　　　　　(B) isn't there
(C) has there　　　　　　　(D) isn't it

22. I think John has left, _____ ?
(A) don't I　　　　　　　　(B) has he
(C) doesn't he　　　　　　　(D) hasn't he

23. I needn't bring my books here tomorrow, _____ I ?
(A) need　　(B) do　　(C) shall　　(D) needn't

24. They need to be reminded of it, _____ ?
(A) needn't they　　　　　　(B) need they
(C) don't they　　　　　　　(D) doesn't it

25. I take it you won't be coming then, _____ ?
(A) don't I　　　　　　　　(B) doesn't it

```
   (C) will you                 (D) shall I
```

標準答案: 1.(D) 2.(B) 3.(A) 4.(B) 5.(C) 6.(A) 7.(A)
         8.(B) 9.(A) 10.(C) 11.(A) 12.(C) 13.(D) 14.(B)
        15.(D) 16.(B) 17.(B) 18.(A) 19.(A) 20.(A) 21.(C)
        22.(D) 23.(A) 24.(C) 25.(C)

習題講解:

1 . 敘述句中有 be 動詞,反問句中沿用 be 動詞。

2 . had to 在此視爲一般動詞。

3 . 敘述句中有助動詞,反問句中沿用助動詞。

4 . 敘述句中有 there be,反問句中沿用 there be。

5 . 與第一題同理。

6 . 與第三題同理。

7 . 因 You have very little to eat. = You have almost
    nothing to eat. 是否定句。
    比較: You have a little to eat, don't you?

8 . 敘述句中有 ought to, would rather, had better 等助動詞
    片語時,反問句中用其第一個字。

9 . 命令句之後的反問句一律用 will you。

1 0 . 『Let's...』句型之後的反問句一律用 shall we。

1 1 . 此爲一般命令句,故用 will you。

1 2 . 此亦爲一般命令句,故用 will you。

１３．have 在此爲一般動詞。

１４．You'd better = You had better

１５．敘述句中的主詞爲 this, 在反問句中須改爲 it。

１６．與第十五題同理。

１７．敘述句中的助動詞若不止一個, 反問句中用第一個助動詞。

１８．此處 used 視爲一般動詞。

１９．hardly 爲否定副詞。

２０．seldom 爲否定副詞。

２１．There's been = There has been

２２．『I think + that 子句』中以 that 子句來作反問句。

２３．need 用於肯定句是一般動詞, 用於否定句則是助動詞, 無論第幾人稱均不加 s。
例: He needs to go, doesn't he?
   He need not go, need he?
   = He doesn't need to go, does he?

２４．見上題解答。

２５．I take it (that) ... = I think (that) ...

常春藤升學系列（7）

常春藤英文文法（下）

編　　著：賴世雄
編　　輯：陳文華
英文編輯：Carl Anthony
美術企劃：何　遙
電　　腦：黎綉珍／陳建球／韓敬亮
顧　　問：高　明／賴陳信愛
法律顧問：王存淦律師／蕭雄淋律師
發行日期：2001年7月再版二刷

發 行 者：常思藤出版社(版權所有・翻印必究)
　　　　　台北市忠孝西路一段 33 號 5 樓
發 行 人：賴世雄
承 印 者：錦龍印刷股份有限公司
行政院新聞局出版事業登記證　局版臺業字第肆捌貳陸號

服務電話：(02)2331-7600
信　　箱：臺北郵政 8-18 號信箱
郵撥帳號：1283563-3　常春藤解析英語雜誌社
售　　價：180 元

＊如有缺頁、裝訂錯誤或破損　請寄回本社更換

常春藤叢書

升學系列

★ 英文閱讀測驗(一) 180元
★ 英文閱讀測驗(二) 180元
★ 常春藤英文文法(上) 180元
★ 常春藤英文文法(下) 180元
★ 英文活用片語 180元
★ 英文解析作文(一) 180元
★ 英文克漏字(一) 180元
★ 英文克漏字(二) 220元
★ 英文精解模擬試題(一) 220元
★ 英文精解模擬試題(二) 220元

★ 英文活用句型翻譯 260元
★ 英文填空測驗 220元
★ 常春藤實用解析字彙(上) 280元
★ 常春藤實用解析字彙(下) 280元
★ 實用解析字彙測驗題 120元
★ 英文連貫式翻譯 180元
★ 常春藤逖克遜成語 220元
★ 近十年大學聯考英文試題解析 280元
★ 英文寫作常犯錯誤辨析 280元

進修系列

● 托福分類式字彙(上) 300元
● 托福分類式字彙(下) 300元
● 常春藤新聞英語 300元
● 旅遊英語會話 200元

● 美語笑話精解 200元
● 世界名著 100元, 全套八冊 800元
● 常春藤活用美語初級篇(上) 200元
● 常春藤活用美語初級篇(下) 200元

有聲系列

◆ 雜誌廣播教學帶 1,300元, 特惠價 1,000元
◆ 雜誌廣播教學朗讀帶(一卷) 100元
◆ 旅遊英語會話每冊 200元, 書及卡帶(二卷) 400元
◆ 常春藤新聞英語每冊 300元, 書及卡帶(四卷) 780元
◆ 常春藤實用解析字彙書(上、下冊)及卡帶(二十卷) 2,060元, 特惠價1,860元
◆ 英文解析作文範文朗讀帶(一卷) 100元
◆ 英文解析作文教學帶全套(二十卷) 2,430元, 特惠價 1,710元(附書及朗讀帶)
◆ 常春藤逖克遜成語每冊 220元, 書及卡帶(八卷) 1,180元, 特惠價 1,080元
◆ 常春藤活用美語初級篇每冊 200元, 書(上、下冊)加卡帶(四卷) 880元

※ 84 年 4 月份起調整新價, 請依此新定價劃撥購書

常春藤解析英語雜誌社

台北市忠孝西路一段 33 號 2F　　　電話 (02)331-7600　　　劃撥帳號: 12835633